P9-BJD-012

Anay

Table of Contents

Essential Question

Why do we need a government?

the White House, Washington, D.C.

My Content Objectives

- Build vocabulary related to government
- Understand the role of government and the jobs of people in government

police officers

soldiers

3

Word	Examples	
dangerous (DANE-juh-res)	 The fire is dangerous.	 The job is dangerous.
forest fire (FOR-est FIRE)	 A forest fire is hot.	 A forest fire is smoky.
gear (GEER)	 This helmet is gear.	 This suit is gear.
parachute (PAIR-uh-shoot)	 He can parachute from a plane.	 He can parachute to the ground.
smoke jumper (SMOKE JUM-per)	 A smoke jumper trains.	 A smoke jumper helps.

My Example	Definition
Visiting a live volcano is dangerous.	**dangerous,** *adjective* not safe
There was a forest fire in California last year.	**forest fire,** *noun* a fire in a wooded area
Fire fighters have gear to extingwish fire.	**gear,** *noun* equipment
I want to go parachuting this summer.	**parachute,** *verb* to jump to the ground using a cloth device
Smoke jumpers have a dangerous job.	**smoke jumper,** *noun* a firefighter who fights forest fires

Smoke Jumpers

A **smoke jumper** fights **forest fires**.

A smoke jumper **parachutes** from a plane.

He or she lands on the ground.

A smoke jumper has a **dangerous** job.

Annotate
- Circle words that you have questions about.
- Underline what happens after smoke jumpers parachute from a plane.

A smoke jumper has **gear**.

A smoke jumper has a helmet.

A smoke jumper trains.

A smoke jumper works with a team.

ThinkSpeakListen

What do smoke jumpers wear to keep them safe?

Smoke Jumpers

Smoke jumpers fight **forest fires** in rough terrain or other places that are difficult to get to.

Smoke jumpers **parachute** from a plane.

They land on a spot near the forest fire. Firefighting tools, food, and water are also dropped by parachute.

Smoke jumpers are a national treasure. Their jobs are hard and very **dangerous**.

Smoke jumpers wear special **gear** to keep them safe.

Padded fireproof suits and helmets with face masks protect jumpers from fire, rocks, and trees.

Being a smoke jumper takes strength and training. Smoke jumpers train in states that have large forests.

They must be able to climb trees, use different saws, and work well on a team.

ThinkSpeakListen

Tell one key detail you learned about smoke jumpers.

Notes

Smoke Jumpers

1   Smoke jumping was introduced in the 1930s by the U.S. Forest Service. It was a way to get to **forest fires** quickly. **Smoke jumpers** are people who are trained to fight fires in rough terrain like mountains or other places that are difficult to get to.

2   Smoke jumpers **parachute** from a plane. They land on a spot near the forest fire. Firefighting tools, food, and water are also dropped by parachute. The tools and supplies will last them for about two days. After that, they will get more.

3   Smoke jumpers wear special **gear** to keep them safe. Padded fireproof suits and helmets with face masks protect jumpers from fire, rocks, and trees. Parachutes are another important piece of equipment. They can be steered by the smoke jumpers. The parachutes' bright colors can be spotted quickly.

4   Being a smoke jumper takes strength and training. Smoke jumpers learn how to jump from a plane, handle a parachute, and land safely. Once on the ground, they must be able to climb trees, use different saws, and work well as a team.

5   Smoke jumpers are a national treasure. Their jobs are hard and very **dangerous**. Next time you hear about a forest fire, you can be sure that smoke jumpers are on the job!

Smoke jumpers train in states that have large forests, like California and Oregon.

Word Map

What does the term smoke jumper mean?

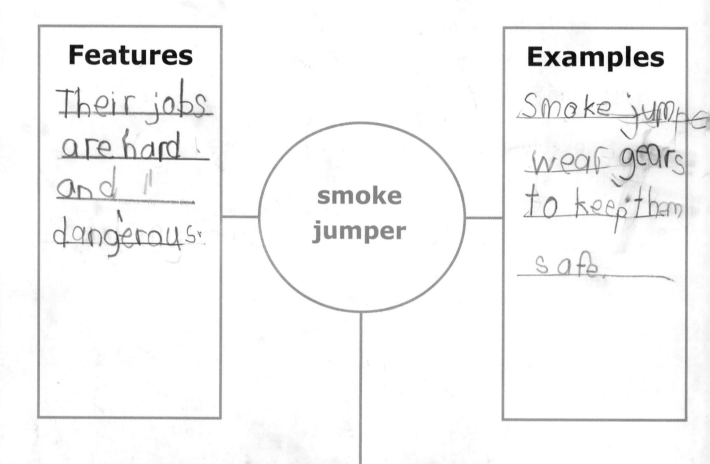

Features
Their jobs
are hard
and
dangerous.

smoke jumper

Examples
Smoke jumper
wear gears
to keep them
safe.

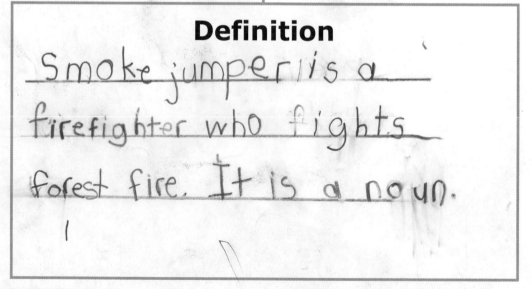

Definition
Smoke jumper is a
firefighter who fights
forest fire. It is a noun.

Main Idea

Main Idea

The passage is about smoke jumpers and their job.

Key Detail

introduced in the 1930.

Key Detail

Smoke jumper train in states that have large forests, like california and Oregon.

Key Detail

They parachute from plane. They wear gears to keep them safe.

Analyze Author's Purpose

Author's Statement	Facts and Details

Text Evidence Questions

1. What is a smoke jumper?

Smoke jumper is a firefighter who fights forest fire.

Text Evidence:

Smoke jumpers are people who are trained to fight fires in rough terrain like mountains or other places difficult to reach.

2. Why do smoke jumpers wear special gear?

Text Evidence:

Smoke jumpers wear special gear to keep them safe.

3. How do smoke jumpers get to forest fires?

Smoke jumpers parachute from the plane.

Text Evidence:

They land on a spot near the forest fire.

4. What does the author of this text think about smoke jumpers? How can you tell?

The author thinks high about smoke jumpers They are national treasure.

Text Evidence:

Next time when you hear about forest fire, you can be make sure they are on the job.

Word	Examples	
government (GUH-vern-ment)	Our government makes plans.	Our government makes laws.
judge (JUJ)	A judge listens in court.	A judge decides in court.
jury (JER-ee)	A jury listens in court.	A jury decides in court.
law (LAW)	This rule is a law.	This rule is a law.
police officer (puh-LEES AU-fih-ser)	 She is a police officer.	 He is a police officer.

My Example	Definition
	government, *noun* a group of people who run a city, state, or country
	judge, *noun* a person who makes the final decision in court
	jury, *noun* a group of people who help make a decision in court
	law, *noun* a rule
	police officer, *noun* a person who works for the government enforcing laws

Our Government's Laws

by Kathy Furgang

We have a **government**.

Our government makes **laws**.

A law is a rule.

We must wear seat belts. This is a law.

Annotate
- Circle words that you have questions about.
- Underline the definition for the word *law*.

We must not speed.
This is a law.

A **police officer** makes sure
we follow the laws.

A **judge** makes sure we
follow the laws.

A **jury** makes sure we
follow the laws.

ThinkSpeakListen
Explain what governments are and what governments do.

Our Government's Laws

by Kathy Furgang

A **government** is a group of people who work together to make important decisions for a country.

A government writes **laws**. A law is a rule that everyone has to follow.

Laws tell people what they can and cannot do. A government makes laws to keep people safe.

State governments have seat belt laws. Every person in a car must wear a seat belt.

There are laws about how fast a car can go and where a car can be parked.

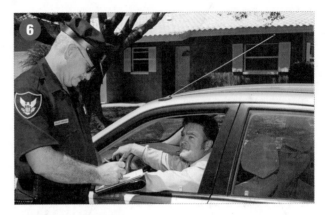

Police officers make sure people follow the laws.

If a law is broken, a person goes to court. A **judge** is in charge and knows all about laws.

A **jury** is a group of people. They listen to court cases. A judge and jury decide if the person broke the law.

ThinkSpeakListen

What do a judge and jury do?

Our Government's Laws

by Kathy Furgang

Notes

They wear seat belt.

They were beautyful where are you?

1   Every country has a **government**. A government is a group of people who work together to make important decisions for the country. All governments make **laws**. A law is a rule that everyone has to follow. A government makes laws to keep people safe.

2   Laws help the government keep order. Laws tell people what they can and cannot do. There are many laws about car seat belts. Every child in a car must wear a seat belt. In most states, adults must wear seat belts too.

3   **Police officers** work for the government. They make sure people follow the laws. There are many laws about driving. There are laws about how fast a car can go. There are laws about where a car can be parked.

4   If a law is broken, a person must go to court. In a courtroom, a **judge** is in charge and knows all about laws. A **jury** is a group of people who listen to court cases. The judge and jury listen to decide if the person broke the law. Then the judge decides what happens to a person who did break the law.

Word Web

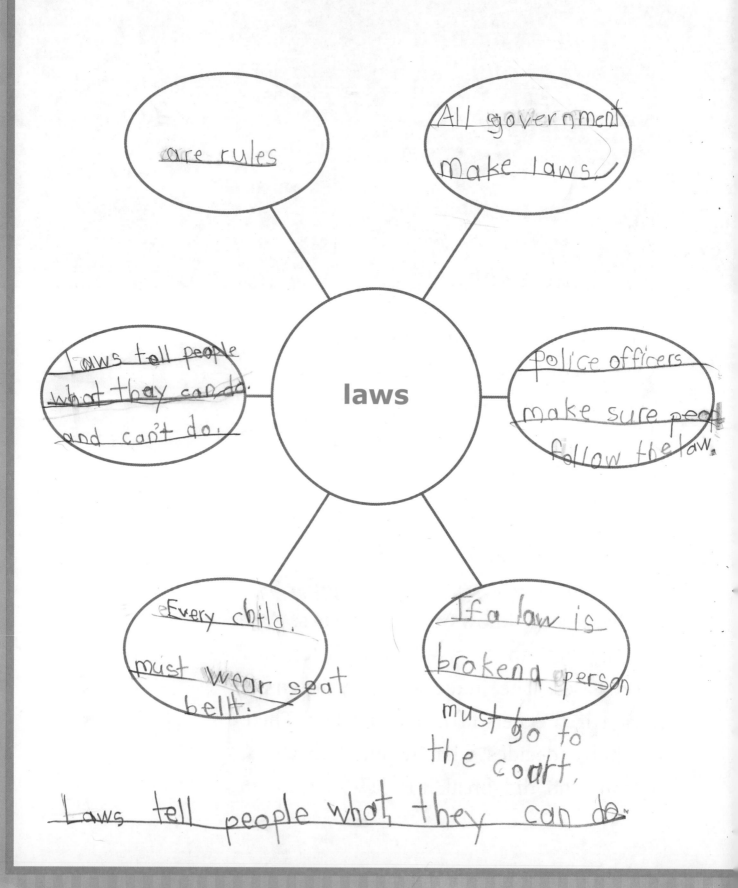

are rules

All government make laws.

Laws tell people what they can do and can't do.

laws

Police officers make sure people follow the law.

Every child must wear seat belt.

If a law is broken a person must go to the court.

Laws tell people what they can do.

Main Idea

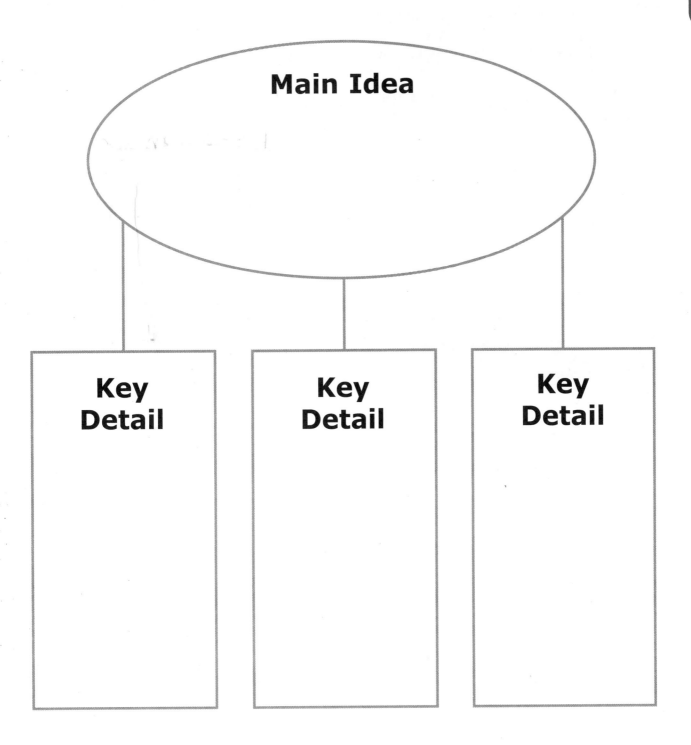

Main Idea

Key Detail

Key Detail

Key Detail

Use Graphic Features

1 **Why do we have this law?**

We have to put on the seat belt to keep people safe during accidents to avoid injury.

2 **Who makes sure people follow laws?**

_____

_____

_____

3 **What happens when people break laws?**

_____

_____

_____

Compare and Contrast

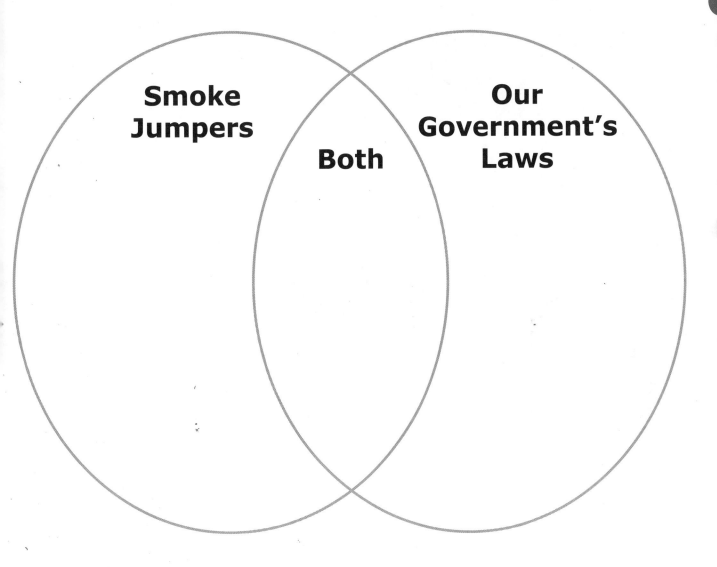

Smoke Jumpers

Both

Our Government's Laws

Word	Examples
code (KODE)	 A code has symbols. A code has letters.
colonies (KAH-luh-neez)	 The British had colonies. The British had colonies.
message (MEH-sij)	The man has a message. The boy has a message.
urgent (ER-jent)	 The message was urgent. The message was urgent.

My Example	Definition
	code, *noun* a secret system of words, letters, or symbols
	colonies, *noun* areas of land owned by a distant government
	message, *noun* a written or spoken communication
	urgent, *adjective* needing instant attention

Getting a Message to General Washington
by Susan Shafer

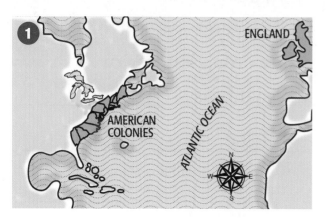

The **colonies** had a problem.
They wanted to be free.

The colonies had a war.
They wanted to win.

They had a plan.

The plan would work.

Annotate
- Circle words that you have questions about.
- Underline the problem that the colonies had.

He had a secret **message**.
The message had a **code**.

The men could not read it.
They did not know the code.

He got the **urgent** message.

The plan would work.

ThinkSpeakListen
Why is the message written in a secret code?

Getting a Message to General Washington by Susan Shafer

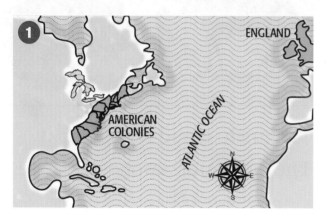

In 1776, the **colonies** were ruled by England. The people in the colonies wanted to be free.

It was the afternoon of December 23, 1776. Ben Franklin was telling his helper, Tom, about the Revolutionary War.

"Washington has a plan to defeat the British. But we don't know how we can get it to work," said Franklin.

Franklin explained, "See this map? General Washington wants to cross the river and make a surprise attack. He needs boats to cross the river!"

"The boats will arrive in two days. Here," he said, "take this **message** to General Washington. It is in a secret **code**."

A British soldier found the message, but only someone who knew the code could figure it out. Tom quickly went on his way.

"General Washington," said Tom, "I have an **urgent** letter." Tom handed the general the paper.

"The boats will be here by 6 a.m. on Christmas. Good work," said Washington.

ThinkSpeakListen

What problem does Tom help Benjamin Franklin solve?

How does Tom help solve the problem?

Getting a Message to General Washington

by Susan Shafer

Notes

1   It was the afternoon of December 23, 1776. Ben Franklin was telling his helper, Tom, about the Revolutionary War. At that time, the country was made up of thirteen **colonies**. The colonies were ruled by England. The British treated the colonists badly, so the colonists declared war on England. They wanted to be free and rule themselves.

2   "We have a problem," Franklin told Tom. "General Washington has lost several battles," explained Franklin. "So, after one and a half years, we are close to losing the war."

3   "What can we do?" asked Tom.

4   Franklin explained, "See this map? Washington is here and the enemy is on the other side. Washington wants to cross the river on Christmas and make a surprise attack."

5   "Washington needs boats to cross the river! I need to get him this **message** that the boats will arrive in two days." Franklin held up a note. "Here," he said, "take this message to Washington. It is written in a secret **code**."

6   About four miles into his trip, Tom spotted a band of British soldiers. The soldiers went through Tom's pockets. They found Franklin's secret message to Washington, but only someone who knew the code could figure it out. Tom quickly went on his way and arrived at Washington's camp.

7   "General Washington," said Tom, "I have an **urgent** letter from Mr. Franklin." Tom handed the general the paper.

8   "The boats will be here by 6 a.m. on Christmas. Good work," said Washington. "You are a patriot."

35

Word Map

What does the word code mean?

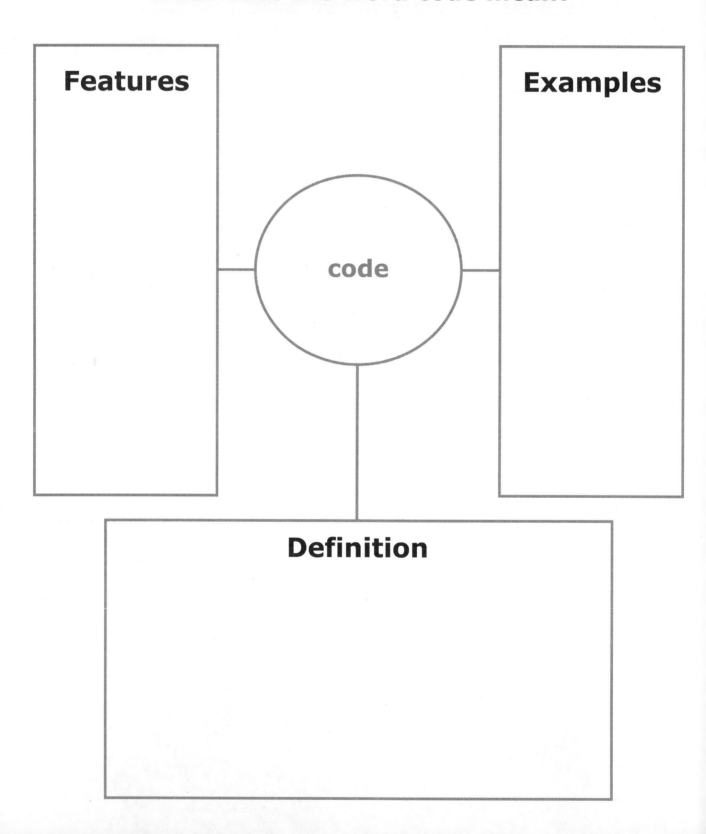

Features

Examples

code

Definition

Recount Story Events

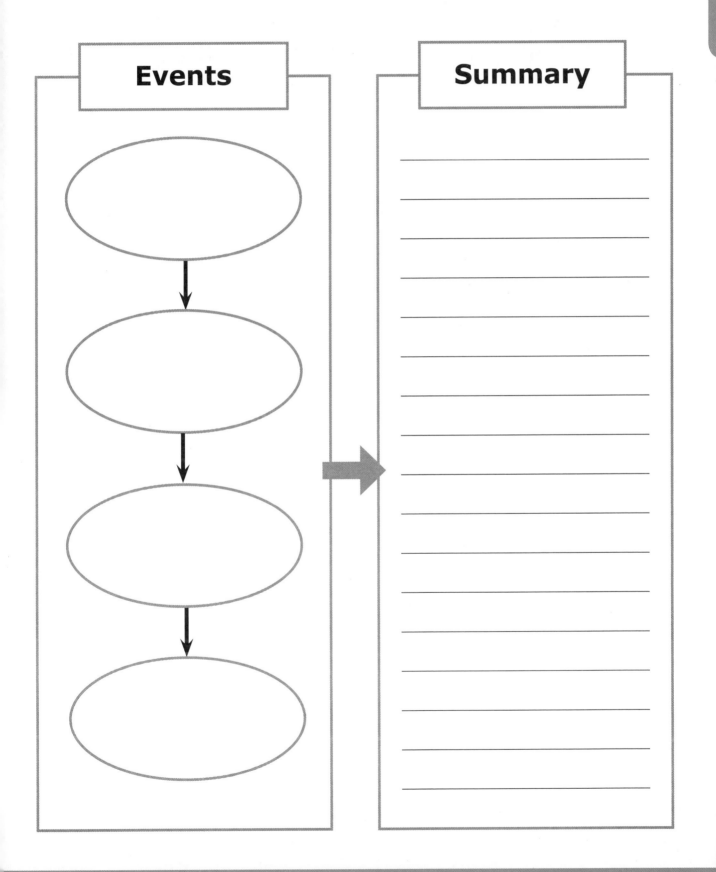

Events

Summary

Analyze Points of View

Character	Point of View
Tom	
Ben Franklin	

Text Evidence Questions

1. Why did the colonies declare war on Britain?

_____

Text Evidence:

_____

_____

_____

2. How does Tom help Ben Franklin?

_____

Text Evidence:

_____

_____

_____

3. Why couldn't the British soldiers read the message?

_____

Text Evidence:

_____

_____

_____

4. What is the problem in this story?

_____

Text Evidence:

_____

_____

_____

Essential Question

What can we learn when we face problems?

a scary bear

My Content Objectives

- Build vocabulary related to solving problems
- Understand how problems teach people lessons about life

a lost slipper

a hungry wolf

41

Word	Examples	
bones (BONEZ)	A fish has bones.	A person has bones.
festival (FES-tih-vul)	The festival has dancing.	The festival has lights.
grant (GRANT)	The bones grant a wish.	The fairies grant a wish.
slippers (SLIH-perz)	These are slippers.	These are slippers.
supper (SUH-per)	They eat supper.	They eat supper.

My Example	Definition
	bones, *noun* the hard parts that frame the body
	festival, *noun* a big celebration
	grant, *verb* give or allow
	slippers, *noun* shoes that slide on
	supper, *noun* an evening meal

Yeh-Shen

retold by Nell Wilson

The girl had a fish.

Her stepmother cooked the fish for **supper**.

The girl was sad.

"The **bones** will **grant** you a wish," said the old man.

Soon it was time for the **festival**. She wanted to go.

Annotate
- Circle words that you have questions about.
- Underline what happens to Yeh-Shen's fish.

5

The bones granted her wish.

6

They gave her a dress and **slippers**.

7

She went to the festival. Her slipper fell off.

8

The king found the slipper.

ThinkSpeakListen

Summarize the story.

Yeh-Shen

retold by Nell Wilson

Once upon a time, there was a girl named Yeh-Shen. Her only friend was a goldfish.

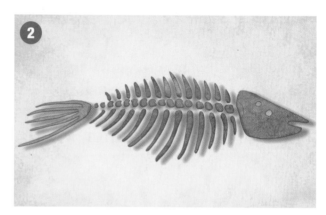

One day, her stepmother killed the fish and served him for **supper**.

"Gather the fish's **bones**," an old man said. "They have great power and can **grant** your wishes."

Soon it was time for the **festival**. Yeh-Shen wanted to attend, but she had only a plain, drab dress to wear.

46

5

Yeh-Shen asked the bones for help. Her old dress and shoes disappeared. In their place were a beautiful dress and golden **slippers**!

6

At the festival, Yeh-Shen was noticed by all. She saw her stepsister staring at her and ran away quickly.

7

As she did, one of her slippers fell off. The king wanted to find the slipper's owner.

8

When the king saw that the slipper fit Yeh-Shen, he proposed. They lived happily ever after.

ThinkSpeakListen

Summarize the story, using key details.

Remember to annotate as you read.

Notes

Yeh-Shen

retold by Nell Wilson

1   Once upon a time, there was a girl named Yeh-Shen. She lived with her mean stepmother and stepsister. The two women mistreated Yeh-Shen because they were jealous of her beauty.

2   Yeh-Shen's only friend was a goldfish. However, one day, her stepmother did the unkindest thing of all. She killed the fish and served him for **supper**.

3   As Yeh-Shen mourned for her friend, an old man suddenly appeared. "Gather the fish's **bones**," he said. "They have great power and can **grant** your wishes."

4   Soon it was time for the Spring **Festival**, where young people went to find husbands and wives. Yeh-Shen wanted to attend. Alas, she had nothing but her plain, drab dress to wear.

5   Yeh-Shen asked the bones for help. Her old dress and shoes disappeared immediately. In their place were a beautiful dress and golden **slippers**!

6   At the festival, Yeh-Shen was noticed by all, even the king! However, Yeh-Shen saw her stepsister staring at her, so she ran away quickly. As she did, one of her slippers fell off.

7   The king wanted to find the slipper's owner. Every woman came to the palace to try it on, but no one's foot could fit!

8   One night, Yeh-Shen crept into the palace. She grabbed the slipper and returned home. She didn't see the king following her. When the king saw that the slipper fit Yeh-Shen, he proposed. Naturally, they lived happily ever after!

Word Map

What does the word festival mean?

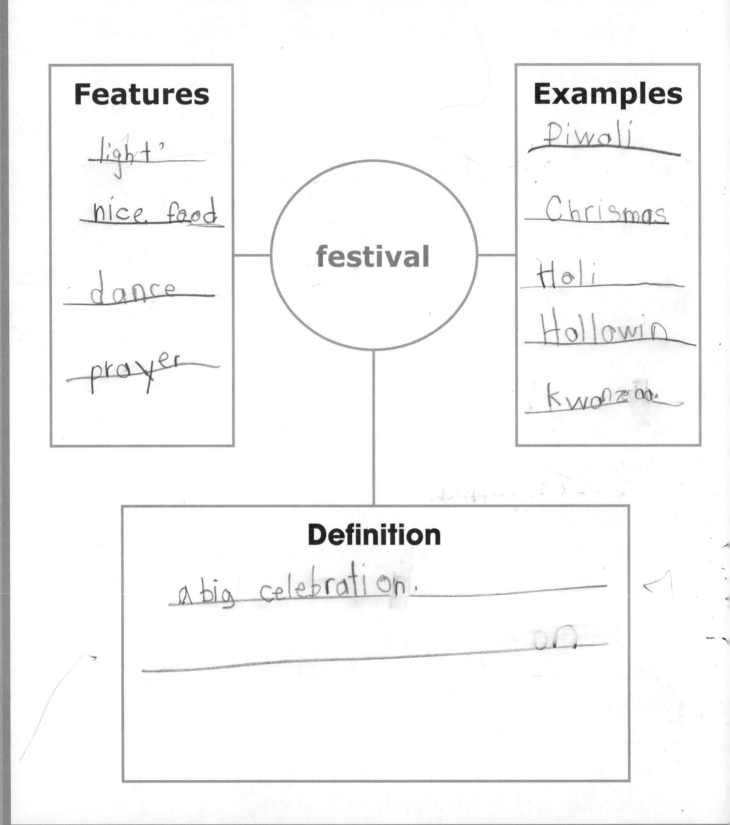

Features

light'

nice food

dance

prayer

festival

Examples

Diwali

Chrismas

Holi

Hollowin

Kwonzaa

Definition

a big celebration.

on

Recount Story Events

Events

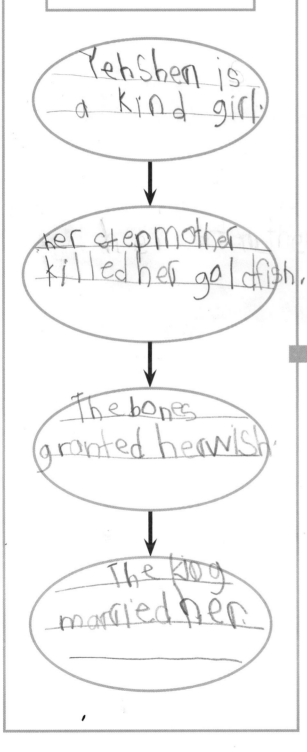

Yeh Shen is a kind girl.

her stepmother killed her goldfish.

The bones granted her wish.

The king married her.

Summary

Yeh shen's step-mother killed her friend, goldfish. The bones of the fish had magic power. She got beautiful dress for the festival. She left her slippers at the festival. The king found her slippers. The king proposed her. They lived happily ever after!

Analyze Character Actions

Character	Actions
Yeh-Shen	She mourned for her friend She asked for a beautiful dress. She married the king.
stepmother	She killed Yeh-Shen's fish and gave him for the supper.

Analyze Story Elements

Setting	Characters

Problem

Solution

Word	Examples	
bad-tempered (BAD-TEM-perd)	The troll is bad-tempered.	The troll is bad-tempered.
bridge (BRIJ)	There is a bridge.	There is a bridge.
decided (dih-SY-ded)	The goat decided to cross.	The goat decided to cross.
rushed (RUSHT)	The goat rushed.	The goat rushed.

My Example	Definition
	bad-tempered, *adjective* easily upset
	bridge, *noun* a structure over water connected to land
	decided, *verb* made a decision
	rushed, *verb* charged

The Three Billy Goats Gruff

retold by Winston Ramos

There was a little goat.
There was a medium goat.
There was a big goat.

They had no grass to eat.

They were hungry. They **decided** to cross the **bridge**.

A **bad-tempered** troll lived under the bridge.

Annotate

- Circle words that you have questions about.
- Underline what happens to the troll.

56

5

He wanted to eat the little goat. He decided to wait.

6

He wanted to eat the medium goat. He decided to wait.

7

He wanted to eat the big goat. The big goat **rushed**.

8

The troll tumbled off the bridge.

ThinkSpeakListen

Tell what happens when the big goat sees the troll.

The Three Billy Goats Gruff

retold by Winston Ramos

Once upon a time, there were three Billy Goats Gruff: a little goat, a medium goat, and a big goat.

The goats did not have enough to eat. Over the **bridge**, the grass was green and sweet.

One day the goats were so hungry they **decided** to cross the bridge.

Under the bridge lived a **bad-tempered** troll. He would not let the goats cross the bridge.

Annotate

- Circle words that you have questions about.
- Underline why the Billy Goats Gruff cross the bridge.

Little Goat went over the bridge. "Please don't eat me. Wait for my brother. He is bigger," said Little Goat. "Be off with you," Troll said.

Medium Goat went over the bridge. "Don't eat me. My brother is much bigger," Medium Goat said. "Oh! Then be off with you," Troll said.

Then Great Big Billy Goat Gruff crossed the bridge. He **rushed** at Troll.

"Ay!" cried Troll. He tumbled off the bridge. Down he went into the deep water under the bridge.

ThinkSpeakListen
Tell what happens when Great Big Billy Goat Gruff sees Troll.

Notes

The Three Billy Goats Gruff

retold by Winston Ramos

1   Once upon a time there were three Billy Goats Gruff that lived on a hillside. The grass had turned brown and dry. The goats did not have enough to eat.

2   Over the **bridge** on another hill, the grass was green and sweet. Under the bridge lived a **bad-tempered** troll. He would not let the goats cross the bridge. The three Billy Goats Gruff grew hungrier.

3   One day the goats were so hungry they **decided** to cross the bridge. Little Billy Goat Gruff went over the bridge.

4   "WHO'S THAT CROSSING OVER MY BRIDGE?" shouted Troll.

5   "Just me," said Little Billy Goat Gruff. "I am very hungry."

6   "Well, I am very hungry too," said Troll. "I WILL EAT YOU UP!"

7   "OH! Please don't eat me. Wait for my brother. Medium Billy Goat Gruff is bigger," replied Little Billy Goat Gruff.

8   "Oh! Then be off with you," Troll said.

9   Then Medium Billy Goat Gruff crossed. "WHO'S THAT CROSSING OVER MY BRIDGE?" shouted Troll again. "I WILL EAT YOU UP!"

10   "Don't eat me. Wait for my brother. Great Big Billy Goat Gruff is much bigger," said Medium Billy Goat Gruff.

11   "Oh! Then be off with you," Troll said.

12   Then Great Big Billy Goat Gruff began to cross the bridge. "WHO'S THAT CROSSING OVER MY BRIDGE?" screamed Troll.

13   "You know it is I," called out Great Big Billy Goat Gruff.

14   Troll climbed up on the bridge. Great Big Billy Goat Gruff **rushed** at him.

15   "Ay!" cried Troll. He tumbled off the bridge. Down he went into the deep water under the bridge.

Word Web

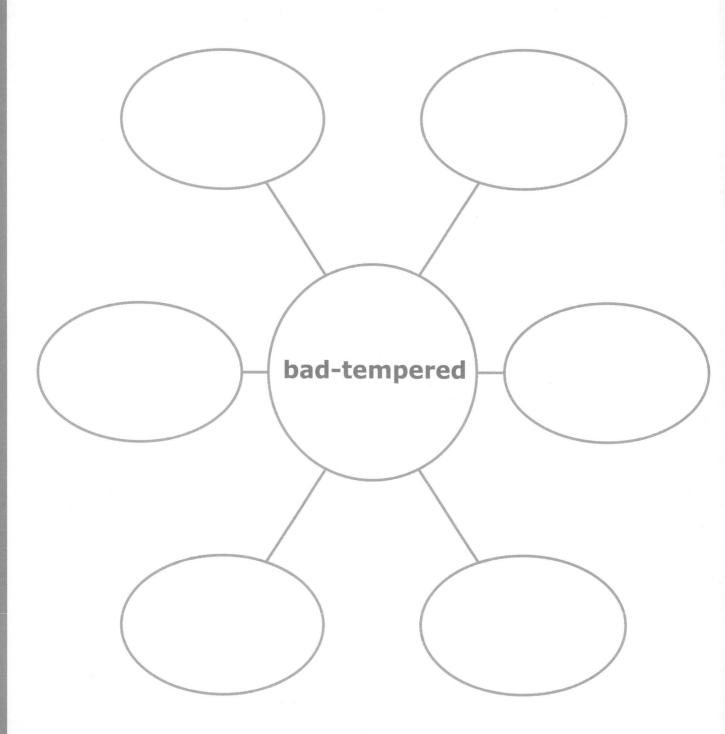

bad-tempered

Main Message

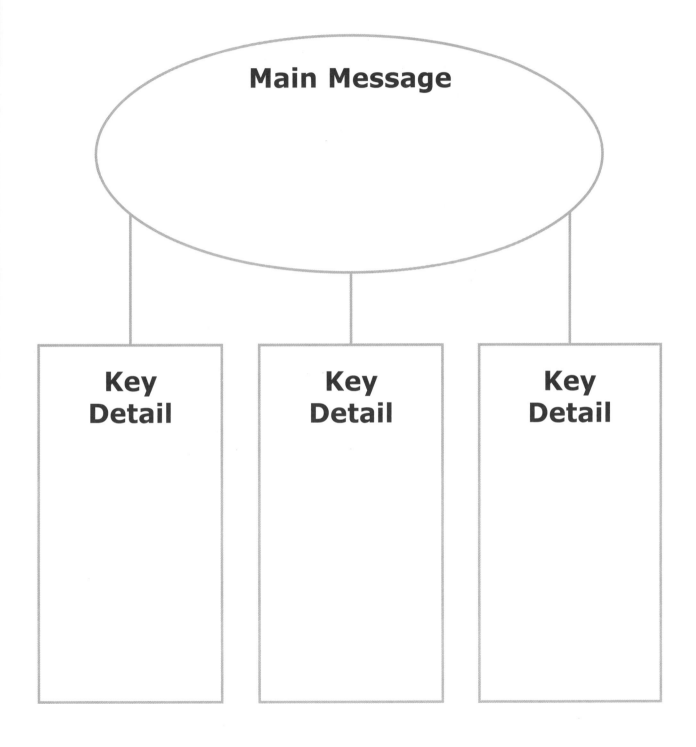

Main Message

Key Detail

Key Detail

Key Detail

Analyze Character

Character	Traits and Actions
Little Goat	
Troll	

Analyze Story Elements

Setting	Characters

Problem

Solution

Word	Examples	
ad (AD)	 The sign had an ad.	 The sign had an ad.
greeter (GREE-ter)	 A greeter says, "Hello!"	 A greeter says, "Welcome!"
job (JAHB)	 The troll has a job.	 The troll has a job.
politeness (puh-LITE-nes)	 The troll learned politeness.	 The troll learned politeness.

My Example	Definition
	ad, *noun* a message that promotes a product
	greeter, *noun* someone who welcomes others
	job, *noun* a duty or task
	politeness, *noun* behavior that is nice and friendly

The Troll Returns

by Jeffrey Fuerst

The troll sees an **ad** for **Politeness** School.

The troll works hard.

The troll is nice. He is not mean.

He gets a **job**. He is a **greeter** at the bridge.

Annotate

- Circle words that you have questions about.
- Underline clues that help you understand what those words mean.

He says, "Hello!"
The goats do not say,
"Hello."

The troll gets mad.

The big goat gives him a
new job.

He keeps the goats safe.

ThinkSpeakListen

What does the big goat do to help the troll?

The Troll Returns

by Jeffrey Fuerst

1 Once upon a time, a mean Troll guarded a bridge over a river. Troll saw an **ad** for **Politeness** School.

2 Politeness School was hard work. Troll was the best student in the class!

3 Troll was now nice. He said, "Hello, goats. Do not run. I am not mean anymore."

4 Great Big Billy Goat Gruff said to Troll, "Since you are nice, I have a **job** for you. You can be the **greeter** at the bridge."

"I would like that job!" said Troll. And he did—at first. But not once did a goat say, "Thank you" or "Have a nice day" to Troll.

"That is it!" yelled Troll. "If you can't be polite and say hello, get off my bridge!"

"Wait," said Great Big Billy Goat Gruff. "I have a better job for you. You can keep billy goats away from the water."

From that day on, Troll roared, "Stay away! Keep out!" Then he added, "Have a nice day."

ThinkSpeakListen

Compare Troll from before Politeness School with Troll after Politeness School.

The Troll Returns

by Jeffrey Fuerst

1   Once upon a time, a mean troll guarded a bridge over a river. Great Big Billy Goat Gruff knocked Troll off that bridge. Troll fell into the river. "It's my bridge!" yelled Troll as he went down the river. He was so mad!

2   Then Troll saw an **ad** for **Politeness** School. "Come to Politeness School. Learn to be nice."

3   "Oh, well," said Troll, "I might as well try it." Politeness School was hard work. Troll learned to smile. He learned to say, "Please," "Thank you," and "Have a nice day." Troll was now nice and did not get mad anymore. He said, "Hello, goats."

4   "Oh, no! Troll is back!" cried a tiny billy goat. "Run for your life."

5   "Wait," said Troll. "Do not run. I am not mean anymore. I will not yell or roar." Great Big Billy Goat Gruff looked at the smiling Troll. "Since you are nice, I have a **job** for you. You can be the **greeter** at the bridge. When the goats cross, you can say, 'Hello! Have a nice day.' When they cross back, you can say, 'Thank you for coming.'"

6   "I would like that job!" said Troll. And he did—at first. *I am nice to the goats,* Troll thought. *I am polite. But not once has a goat said, "Thank you" to me.*

7   "That is it!" yelled Troll. "Get off my bridge!"

8   "Wait," said Great Big Billy Goat Gruff. "We were wrong not to say, 'thank you.' Your new job is to keep us away from the water. We are not good swimmers."

9   From that day forward, Troll roared, "Stay away! Keep out!" whenever a billy goat came near the lake. Then he added, "Have a nice day."

Word Map

What does the word politeness mean?

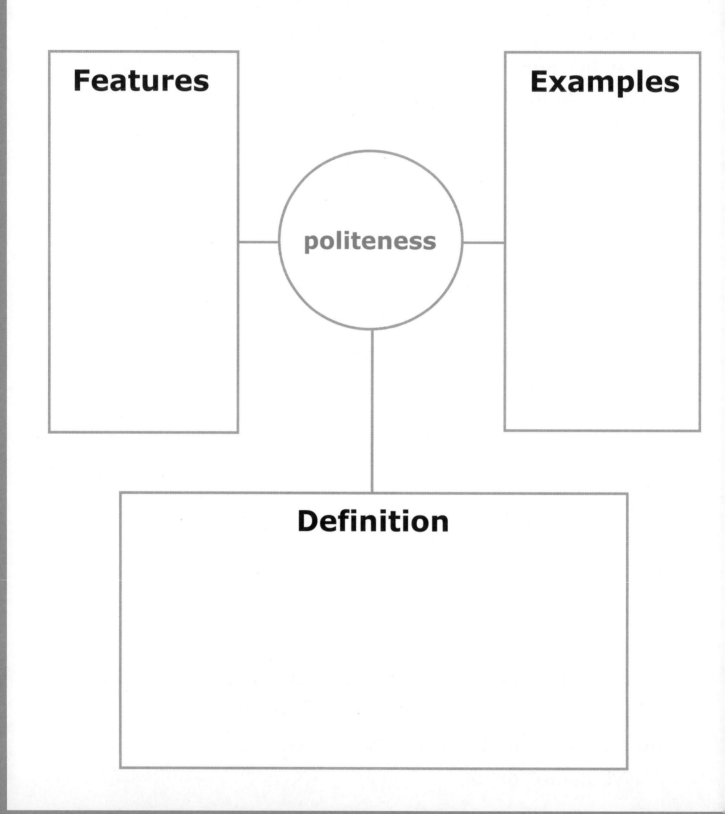

Features

Examples

politeness

Definition

Recount Story Events

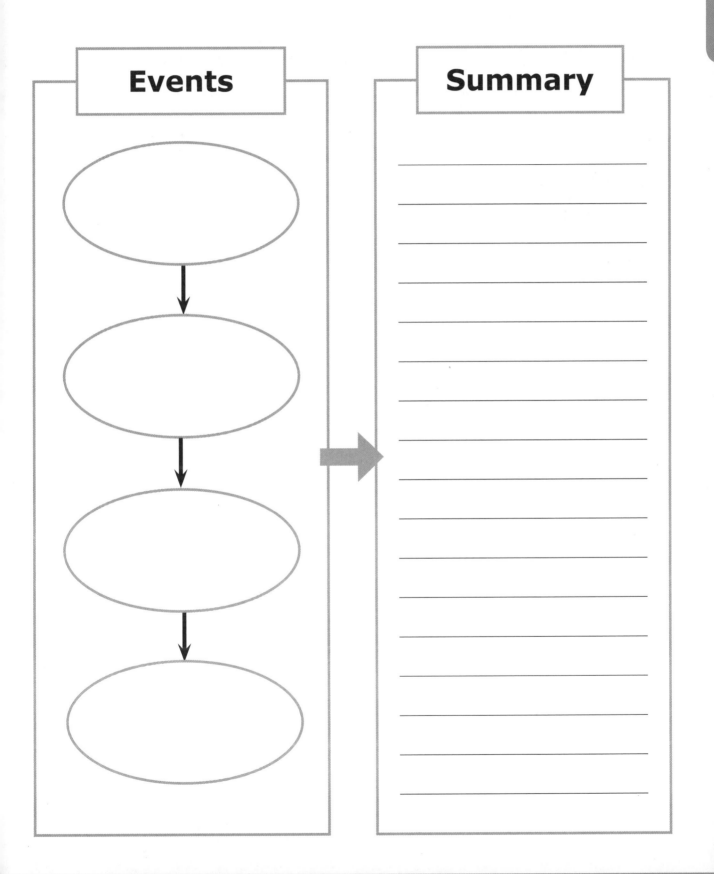

Events

Summary

Analyze Points of View

Character	Point of View
Troll	
Great Big Billy Goat Gruff	

Compare and Contrast

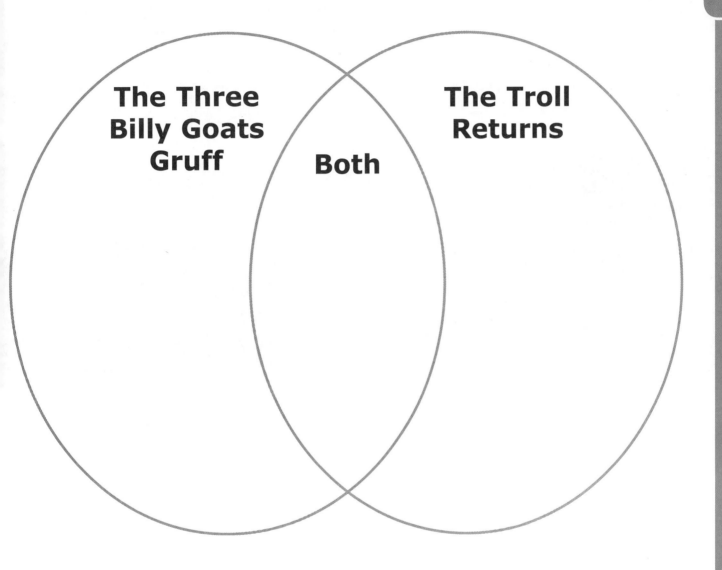

The Three
Billy Goats
Gruff

Both

The Troll
Returns

Essential Question

How do living things get what they need to survive?

My Content Objectives

- Build vocabulary related to plants and animals in different habitats around the world

- Compare and contrast habitats around the world

desert

coral reef

wetland

Word	Examples
emperor penguin (EM-per-er PEN-gwin)	An emperor penguin stands. / An emperor penguin swims.
hatch (HACH)	A chicken can hatch. / A penguin can hatch.
huddle (HUH-dul)	They huddle to stay close. / They huddle to stay warm.
waddle (WAH-dul)	The penguins waddle. / The penguins waddle.

My Example	Definition
	emperor penguin, *noun* a type of bird that lives in Antarctica
	hatch, *verb* to be born from an egg
	huddle, *verb* to crowd together
	waddle, *verb* to walk side to side

The Coldest Place on Earth

The coldest place on Earth is Antarctica.

The **emperor penguin** lives there.

These birds **waddle** across the ice.

Each mother lays an egg. Then she waddles back to the sea.

Annotate
- Circle words that you have questions about.
- Underline where emperor penguins live.

The fathers wiggle the eggs onto their feet.

They **huddle** to keep warm.

Tap, tap, crack!
The eggs **hatch**.

The penguin families go back to the sea.

ThinkSpeakListen

Look at panel 5. Describe what father penguins do with the eggs.

The Coldest Place on Earth

Antarctica is the iciest, windiest, and emptiest place on Earth. Only a few animals can survive Antarctica's winters.

Meet the **emperor penguin**! These amazing birds spend most of their lives in the freezing-cold sea.

All the penguins **waddle** across the ice when it's time to lay eggs.

Each mother lays one egg and then waddles back to the sea to eat.

84

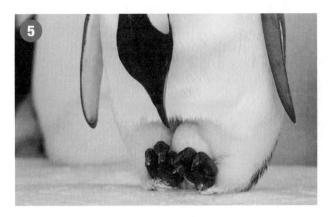

The fathers wiggle the eggs onto their feet, right under their bellies.

All the fathers **huddle** together to keep each other warm.

Then one day, *tap, tap, crack!* The eggs **hatch**.

The mothers come back to feed and care for their chicks. The penguin families return to the sea again.

ThinkSpeakListen

Retell a key detail about emperor penguins.

Remember to annotate as you read.

Notes

barren

The Coldest Place on Earth

1   *Brrrr.* Covered by a thick blanket of snow and ice, Antarctica is the iciest, windiest, and emptiest place on Earth. Its barren landscape has no trees and few plants. Some people visit, but none live there. Only a few tough animals can survive Antarctica's harsh winters. One of them is an amazing bird.

2   Meet the **emperor penguin**! These barrel-shaped birds can't fly. They are too heavy and their wings are too short. They can't walk too well, either. These penguins spend most of their lives in the freezing-cold sea. A thick layer of blubber, or fat, and shiny feathers act like a heavy, waterproof jacket.

3   All the penguins **waddle** across the ice when it's time to lay eggs. Each mother lays one egg and then waddles back to the sea to eat. Who will keep those fragile eggs from breaking or freezing? The fathers wiggle the eggs onto their feet, right under their bellies. There the eggs stay safe and warm.

4   The wind is freezing cold. All the fathers **huddle** together to keep one another warm. Then one day, *tap, tap, crack!* The eggs **hatch**. The mothers come back to feed and care for their chicks. Now it's the fathers' turn to eat. Soon the penguin families will return to the sea again.

Word Map

What do the words emperor penguin mean?

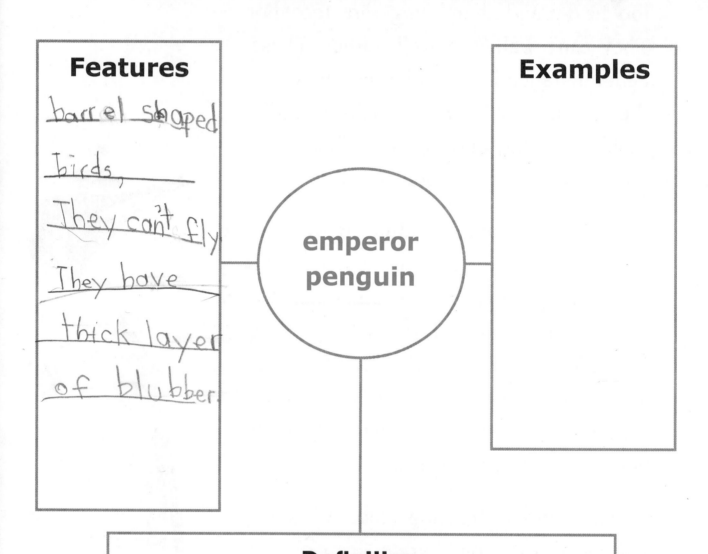

Features

barrel shaped
birds,
They can't fly
They have
thick layer
of blubber.

Examples

emperor penguin

Definition

A type of bird that lives in
Antarctica.

Main Idea

Main Idea

The emperer penguin lives in the coldest place on earth Antarctica.

Detail

They have thick blubber to protect from the cold.

Detail

The father keeps the eggs warm under his belly.

Detail

The Penguin families retur to the sea after hatching.

Use Graphic Features

1 Where do emperor penguins live?

_____

_____

_____

2 Who takes care of the eggs? How?

_____

_____

_____

3 How do emperor penguins stay warm?

_____

_____

_____

Text Evidence Questions

1. What is the climate like in Antarctica?

_____

Text Evidence:

_____

_____

_____

2. What are some characteristics of emperor penguins?

_____

_____

Text Evidence:

_____

_____

_____

3. What happens after a mother penguin lays an egg?

_____

Text Evidence:

_____

_____

4. Who cares for the penguin chicks?

_____

_____

Text Evidence:

_____

_____

Word	Examples	
coral reef (KOR-ul REEF)	 **The coral reef has plants.**	 **The coral reef has fish.**
grassland (GRAS-land)	 **The grassland has grass.**	 **The grassland has water.**
habitat (HA-bih-tat)	 **This habitat is dry.**	 **This habitat is wet.**
rain forest (RANE FOR-est)	 **A rain forest has plants.**	 **A rain forest has animals.**
tundra (TUN-druh)	 **The tundra has animals.**	 **The tundra has snow.**

My Example	Definition
	coral reef, *noun* an ocean habitat made of tiny shells
	grassland, *noun* a grassy plain
	habitat, *noun* a home or environment for living things
	rain forest, *noun* a wet jungle habitat with tall trees
	tundra, *noun* a cold arctic region

Habitats Around the World

by Thea Feldman

A **habitat** is where plants and animals live.

grassland   rain forest   tundra   coral reef

There are habitats around the world.

A **grassland** is a habitat.

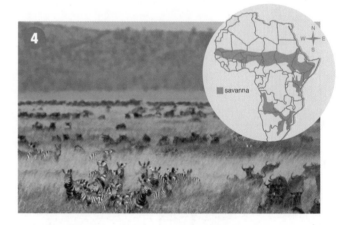

savanna

A grassland in Africa is a savanna.

Annotate
- Circle words that you have questions about.
- Underline what a grassland in Africa is called.

These animals live in the **tundra**.

There are different kinds of forests.

In a **rain forest**, trees and plants are green all year.

A **coral reef** is in the ocean.

ThinkSpeakListen

Summarize what the text is mainly about.

Habitats Around the World

by Thea Feldman

1 A **habitat** is a place where plants and animals live in nature.

2 There are different habitats around the world. Animals and plants live in these habitats.

grassland   rain forest   tundra   coral reef

3 A **grassland** is one habitat. Grasslands are found all over the world. Only the South Pole does not have one.

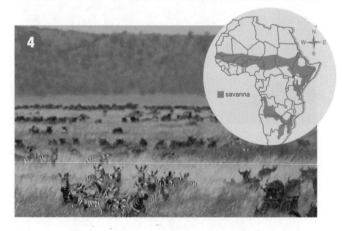

savanna

4 Grasslands in Africa are called "savannas." A savanna has a long, hot, dry season. Animals leave during the dry season.

The world's **tundras** are located near or at the North and South Poles. Polar bears, foxes, seals, and oxen live on the Arctic tundra.

Nearly one-third of the planet is covered by forest habitats. There are many different kinds of forests.

A tropical **rain forest** is hot and rainy. Trees and plants stay green all year long.

A **coral reef** is a place in the ocean. Hundreds of animals and sea plants live in a coral reef.

ThinkSpeakListen

Tell a key detail. Then tell the main idea the detail supports.

Habitats Around the World

by Thea Feldman

1   A **habitat** is a place where plants and animals live in nature. There are different kinds of habitats around the world.

2   A **grassland** is one kind of habitat. Grasslands are found all over the world. Only the South Pole does not have one. Grasslands are lands covered with grass. Many other plants and flowers live there too, but only a few bushes and trees. Most grasslands are flat.

3   Grasslands in Africa are called "savannas." A savanna has a long, hot, dry season. Animals leave home each year during this season. They leave to find food and water. A rainy season starts after the dry season ends. The animals go back home after the rainy season. The rains allow new grass to grow. The animals eat the new grass. There is also rainwater to drink.

4   The **tundra** is a habitat that gets very cold. The world's tundras are all located near or at the North and South Poles. Those are the two coldest places on Earth. The Arctic tundra is near the North Pole. In the winter, even the ground freezes! In the summer, the top layer of soil thaws out. Then plants and flowers grow. Polar bears, foxes, seals, and oxen all live there.

5   Nearly one-third of the planet is covered by forest habitats. There are many different kinds of forests. A tropical **rain forest** is hot and rainy. Trees and other plants stay green all year long.

6   A **coral reef** is a place in the ocean. A coral reef is made of coral, a very tiny animal. Hundreds of other kinds of animals live in a coral reef. Many sea plants live there, too. Coral reefs are found in warm, shallow water.

Word Web

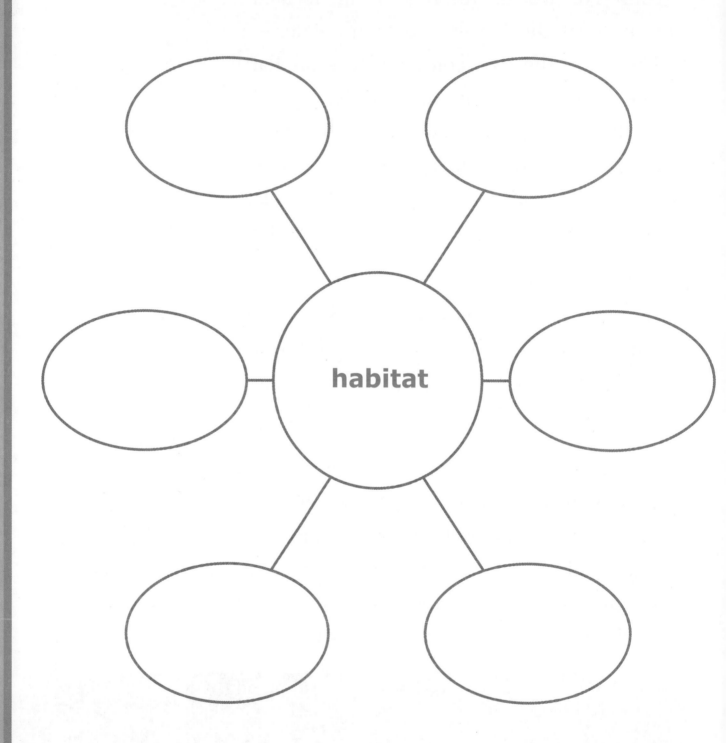

habitat

Main Idea

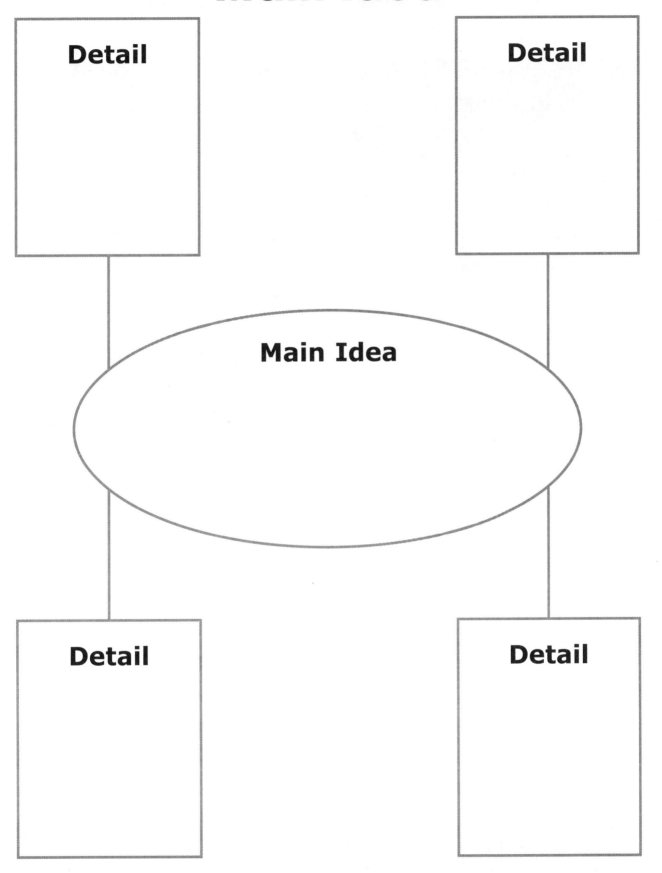

Detail

Detail

Main Idea

Detail

Detail

Use Graphic Features

1 **What is a habitat?**

_____

_____

_____

_____

2 **Where do seals live?**

_____

_____

_____

_____

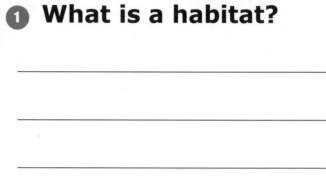

3 **What type of habitat is a savanna? Where can you find one?**

_____

_____

_____

Text Evidence Questions

1. What are the four main habitats discussed in this selection?

_____

_____

Text Evidence:

_____

_____

_____

_____

2. What habitats are dry?

_____

_____

Text Evidence:

_____

_____

3. Why do animals leave during the dry season?

_____

_____

Text Evidence:

_____

_____

4. Where can you find a coral reef?

_____

Text Evidence:

_____

Word	Examples
desert (DEH-zert)	The desert has people. The desert has plants.
disappeared (dis-uh-PEERD)	The kangaroo rat disappeared. The car disappeared.
kangaroo rat (kan-guh-ROO RAT)	This is a kangaroo rat. This is a kangaroo rat.
map (MAP)	They pointed to the map. They looked at the map.

My Example	Definition
	desert, *noun* a dry, sandy habitat with few plants
	disappeared, *verb* went out of sight; vanished
	kangaroo rat, *noun* a type of desert rat
	map, *noun* a visual tool that helps with location and directions

Lost in the Desert

by Thea Feldman

The family was in the **desert**. They looked at a **map**.

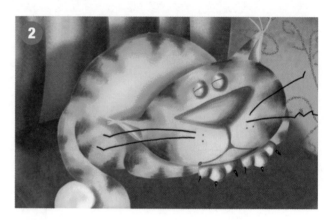

The cat was in the car.

The family got out of the car.

The cat ran outside.

Annotate
- Circle words that you have questions about.
- Underline clues that help you understand what those words mean.

5

The cat saw a **kangaroo rat**.

6

The rat **disappeared**!

7

The cat was lost!

8

The cat saw the car.
He was found!

ThinkSpeakListen

Retell the events that happen in the desert.

Lost in the Desert

by Thea Feldman

Kara's mom showed her the **map**. "Oh yeah," said Kara, "the Sonoran **Desert**."

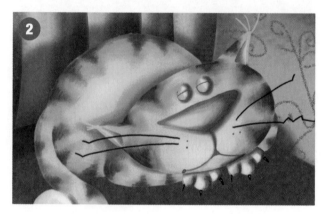

Kara looked over at Fred, the cat napping next to her.

Kara and her parents got out of the car.

Kara's mom opened the car door to grab her camera. At the same time, Fred woke up and slipped outside.

A **kangaroo rat** dashed right in front of Fred and ran into the brush.

Fred tried to catch the rat, but it **disappeared** into a hole in the ground!

Fred hoped his family would realize he was missing and come back for him before dark.

Fred heard three car doors slam. He heard three voices call, "Fred! Fred! Fred!" and he ran toward the sounds.

ThinkSpeakListen
What happens to Fred at the end of the story?

Notes

bloom meens flawers

Lost in the Desert

by Thea Feldman

1   Kara looked out the car window. "Where are we again?" she asked her parents. Kara's mom showed her the **map**. "We're in the Sonoran **Desert**, in Arizona—on our way to see the organ pipe cactuses in bloom."

2   "Oh yeah," said Kara. Kara looked over at the family cat napping on the seat next to her. "Looks like he'll sleep through the entire vacation!" said Kara.

3   Kara and her parents got out of the air-conditioned car. They saw many tall cactuses with big flowers.

4   "I'm glad we came early, before it gets even hotter," said Kara's mother. At the same time, Fred woke up. Right before Kara's mom closed the door again, he slipped outside. Kara's mother did not notice. Neither did Kara nor her dad.

5   Suddenly a **kangaroo rat** dashed right in front of Fred and ran into the brush. Fred chased it. Just when Fred thought he might catch the rat, it **disappeared** into a hole in the ground! The rat was gone.

6   Fred looked around. He did not see the car. He did not see Kara or her parents. Fred felt the heat on his back and on his paws, too. The ground was so hot!

7   Fred heard three car doors slam. He ran toward the sound. Fred got to the road and saw the car leaving without him. His family thought he was still inside!

8   Fred froze in terror. Suddenly he heard three voices call, "Fred! Fred! Fred!" It was his family! Without looking behind him, he ran toward the sounds. When he got to the car, he scrambled into the backseat.

Word Web

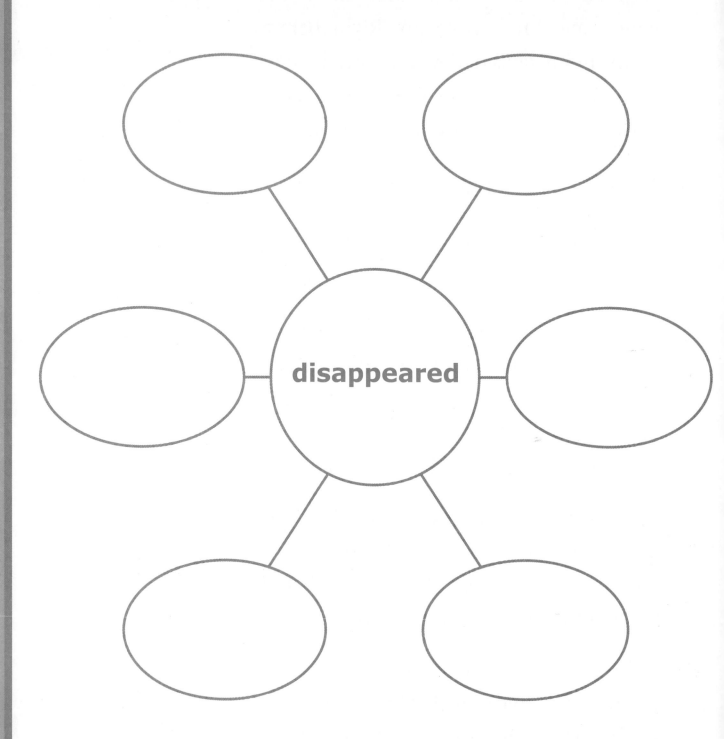

Recount Story Events

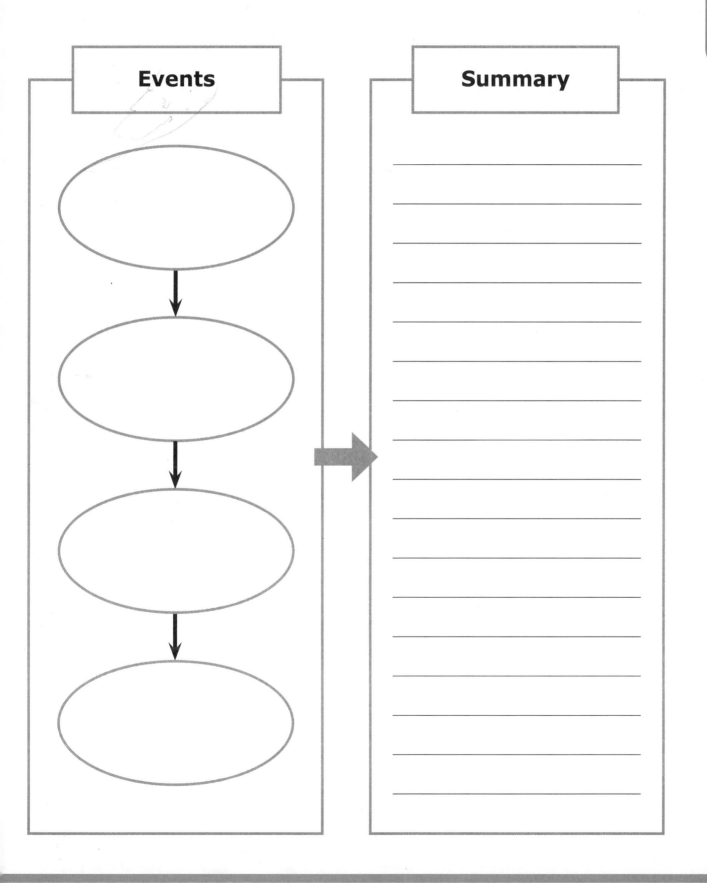

Events

Summary

Text Evidence Questions

1. What is the setting in this story?

_____

Text Evidence:

_____

_____

2. Who are the characters?

_____

_____

Text Evidence:

_____

_____

3. What does Fred see in the desert?

_____

Text Evidence:

_____

_____

4. How did Fred get lost in the desert?

_____

_____

Text Evidence:

_____

_____

Compare and Contrast

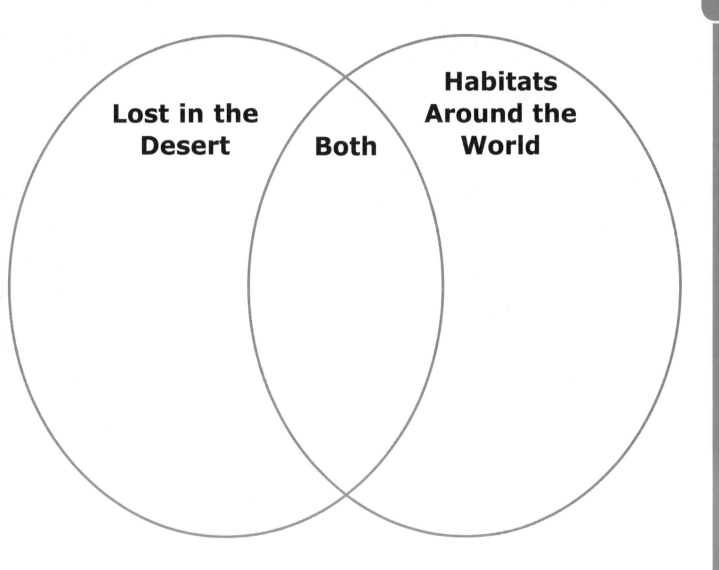

Lost in the
Desert

Both

Habitats
Around the
World

Essential Question

How can a story change depending on who tells it?

Wind and Sun

My Content Objectives

- Understand that characters have different points of view
- Build vocabulary related to how characters solve problems

Ant and Grasshopper

City Mouse and Country Mouse

117

Word	Examples
finish line (FIH-nish LINE)	This is the finish line. This is the finish line.
prize (PRIZE)	He gets a prize. She gets a prize.
race (RASE)	The race is starting. The race is over.
winner (WIH-ner)	He is the winner. She is the winner.

My Example	Definition
	finish line, *noun* a line at the end of a race
	prize, *noun* a reward for accomplishing something
	race, *noun* a competition for runners
	winner, *noun* one who succeeds or gets first place in a contest

How the Beetle Got Its Gorgeous Coat

"I run so fast!"
said the rat.

"I'm not jealous,"
said the beetle.

"Let's have a **race**!"
said the parrot.

"The **winner** will
get a **prize**!"

Annotate

- Circle words that you have questions about.
- Underline what the winner of the race will get.

120

The rat ran fast.

The beetle got to the **finish line** first.

How? She flew.

The coat was her prize!

ThinkSpeakListen

Explain what the rat and the beetle do.

How the Beetle Got Its Gorgeous Coat

"See how quickly I run!" the rat boasted. He often liked to brag.

"I'm not jealous of you," the beetle replied politely.

A parrot had overheard their conversation. "I have an idea!" she exclaimed. "Let's have a **race**!"

"The **winner** will receive a special **prize**, a brightly colored coat in colors of your choice!" she added.

The gray rat ran swiftly.
The beetle crawls so slowly,
he thought. *She can't*
possibly win!

The rat was surprised when
he reached the **finish line**
and found the beetle there!

"How did you do it?"
he asked.

"I flew," she said, spreading
her wings.

The beetle chose a gorgeous
green-and-gold coat—the
same coat she proudly
wears today!

ThinkSpeakListen

Look at panels 6 and 8. Who wins the race? What is the special prize?

How the Beetle Got Its Gorgeous Coat

1 Today, the beetles of Brazil are admired for their beautifully colored coats. However, there was once a time when they wore plain, brown coats.

2 How did their coats change? It all took place long ago. A brown beetle was happily crawling along a wall. Suddenly, a large gray rat ran to her and laughed.

3 "See how quickly I run!" the rat boasted, for he often liked to brag. "You probably envy my speed!"

4 "I'm not jealous of you," the beetle replied politely. "I'm glad that you can run so fast."

5 Meanwhile, a brightly colored parrot had overheard their conversation. "I have an idea!" she exclaimed. "Let's have a **race**!"

6 "The **winner** will receive a unique and special **prize**, a brightly colored coat in colors of your choice!" she added.

7   The rat and beetle were excited. Both wanted a colorful coat.

8   Soon the race began. The gray rat ran swiftly, as usual. *The beetle crawls so slowly,* he thought. *She can't possibly win!*

9   Imagine the rat's surprise when he reached the **finish line** and found the beetle there! "How did you do it?" he asked.

10   "I flew," she said quietly, spreading her wings.

11   "I didn't know you could fly," the rat whispered.

12   Then the beetle chose a gorgeous green-and-gold coat—the same coat she proudly wears today!

Word Map

What does the word race mean?

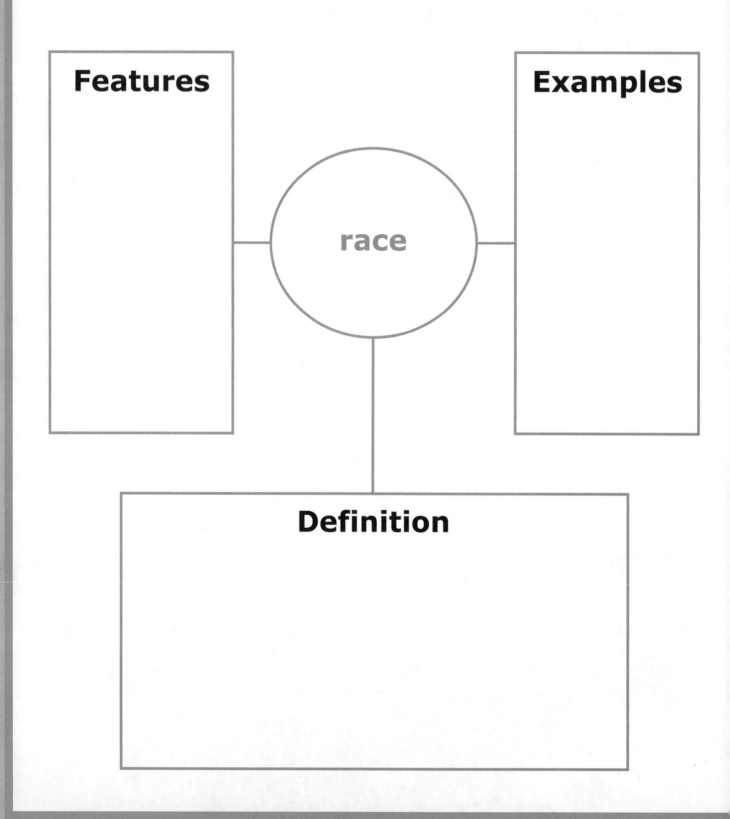

Features

Examples

race

Definition

Main Message

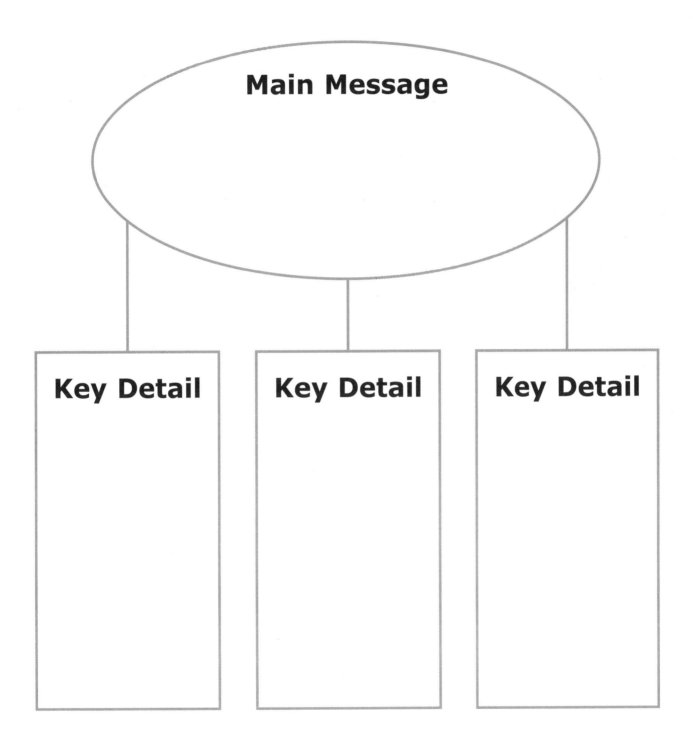

Main Message

Key Detail

Key Detail

Key Detail

127

Analyze Points of View

Character	Point of View
rat	
beetle	

Recount Story Events

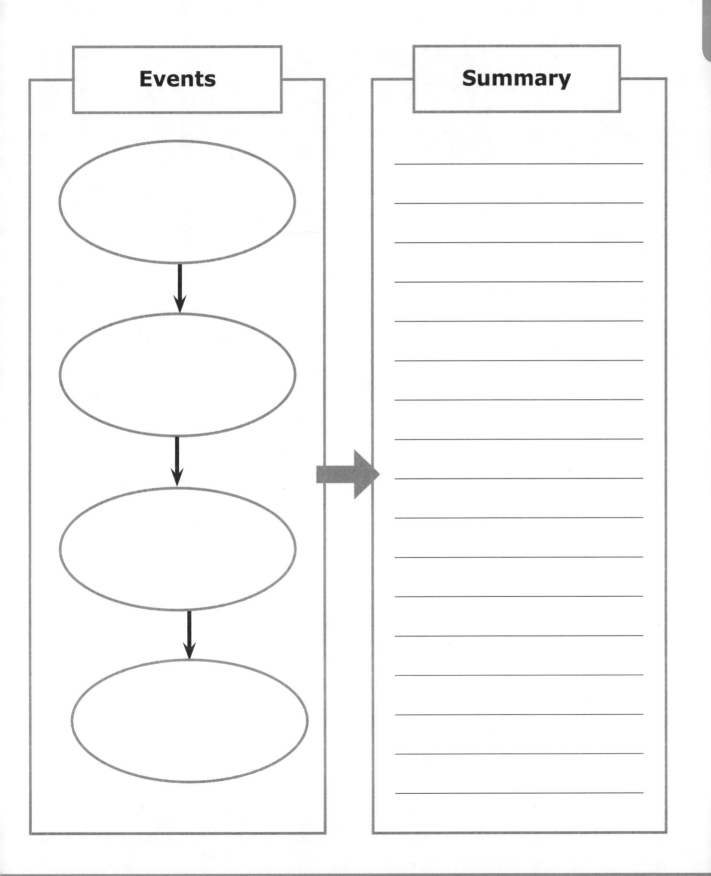

Events

Summary

Word	Examples
butcher (BUH-cher)	The butcher adds the meat. The butcher sells the meat.
delicious (dih-LIH-shes)	The apple is delicious. The soup is delicious.
meal (MEEL)	This is a meal. This is a meal.
village (VIH-lij)	She is ìn the village. He is in the village.

My Example	Definition
	butcher, *noun* a person who sells meat
	delicious, *adjective* tasty
	meal, *noun* a serving of food
	village, *noun* a town or place where people live together

Stone Soup

retold by Winston Ramos

The old man came to a **village**.

He was looking for a **meal** to share.

He filled a pot with water.

He put a stone into the pot.

Annotate
- Circle words that you have questions about.
- Underline what the old man puts in the pot.

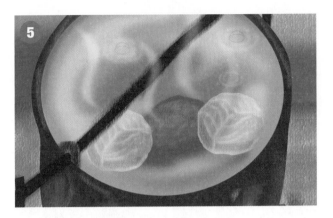

A boy put in cabbage.

A **butcher** put in lamb.

Soon a **delicious** meal was ready.

The village shared the soup.

ThinkSpeakListen

Tell the story's main idea. Give a detail that supports the main idea.

Stone Soup

retold by Winston Ramos

One evening, an old man walked into a **village**.

"I am looking for a place for the night, and a **meal** to share," he said.

He pulled a large pot from his coat. The hungry villagers watched as he filled the pot with water.

When the water was boiling, he dropped a stone into the pot.

"Of course, stone soup with cabbage is even better!"

Soon, a villager added cabbage to the pot.

After that the village **butcher** came. "I was saving this small leg of lamb." He dropped the lamb into the pot.

Several villagers added turnips and carrots to the soup. Before long, a **delicious** meal was ready.

Everyone in the village had a big bowlful of soup. No one went to bed hungry that night.

ThinkSpeakListen

Discuss the lesson that the villagers learn from the old man.

Notes

Stone Soup

retold by Winston Ramos

1   Late one evening long ago, an old man walked into a **village**. "I am looking for a place for the night, and a **meal** to share," he said.

2   Then, with a quick move, like a magician, he pulled a large pot from his coat. The hungry villagers watched as he filled the pot with water.

3   When the water was boiling, he reached into his coat again. This time he took a large stone from a velvet bag. He dropped the stone into the pot.

4   "Is the stone soup really for everyone?" asked a boy.

5   "It is for anyone who wants it," said the old man.

6   News quickly spread through the village. The old man was making stone soup to share with everyone.

7   Soon, a villager approached with a cabbage. "I had a good crop this year," he said. He added the cabbage to the pot.

8   "Wonderful!" cried the old man. "I once had stone soup with cabbage and a piece of lamb as well. It was a feast for a king."

9   Soon after that, the village **butcher** came up to the pot. "I was saving this small leg of lamb for my Sunday dinner. I can make something else then." He dropped the lamb into the pot.

10   In no time at all, several villagers found a turnip or carrot and added them to the soup. Before long, a **delicious** meal was ready. Everyone in the village who wanted stone soup had a big bowlful.

Identify Real-Life Connections Between Words

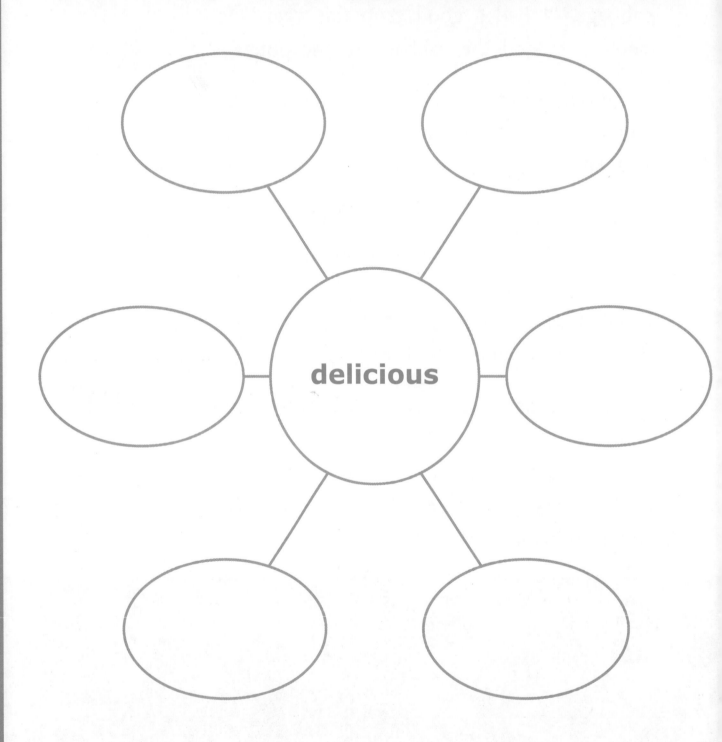

delicious

Main Message

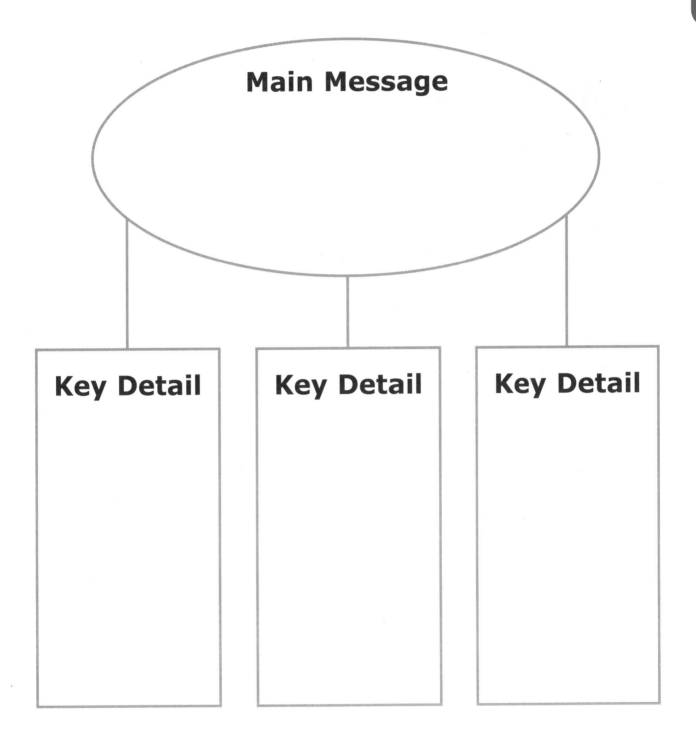

Analyze Character Actions

Character	Actions
old man	
villagers	

Analyze Story Elements

Setting	Characters

Problem

Solution

Word	Examples
eyesore (I-sor)	They see an eyesore. / They clean an eyesore.
garden (GAR-den)	This garden is green. / This garden is colorful.
lot (LAHT)	This is a lot. / This is a lot.
paint (PANTE)	She can paint the rocks. / He can paint the house.

My Example	Definition
	eyesore, *noun* something ugly to look at
	garden, *noun* a piece of land where plants and flowers grow
	lot, *noun* an area of land
	paint, *verb* to brush on a colored liquid

The Stone Garden

by Jeffrey Fuerst

The street had an empty **lot**.

The lot was an **eyesore**.

We can make a **garden**.

He put a stone into the lot.

Annotate

- Circle words that you have questions about.
- Underline clues that help you understand what those words mean.

A girl put in some rocks.

We can **paint** the rocks.

We can plant flowers.

Now we have a garden.

ThinkSpeakListen

Tell about the events that happen in the story.

The Stone Garden

by Jeffrey Fuerst

The people of Yancy Place were proud of their street.

That changed when the gas station closed.

The owners took out the gas tanks.

"This is an **eyesore**!" said the people of Yancy Place.

An old man stepped through the crowd. "This is not an eyesore," he said. "It is a stone **garden**."

He pushed a large stone to the center of the **lot**. "We can put some rocks around the big stone."

"Of course," he said, "to make a stone garden, we can **paint** the rocks different colors."

"To make a stone garden, we can have plants and flowers."

The people of Yancy Place worked all day in the garden.

The old man took one last look at the stone garden and went on his way.

ThinkSpeakListen

Discuss how the old man helps the people of Yancy Place.

The Stone Garden

by Jeffrey Fuerst

1   The people of Yancy Place were proud of their street. That changed when the gas station on the corner closed. All that was left was an empty **lot**. Stones, bricks, broken slate, plastic bottles, and old tires were everywhere.

2   "This is an **eyesore**!" said the people of Yancy Place. An old man in a cloth cap stepped through the crowd. He looked around. "This is not an eyesore," he said. "It is a lovely stone **garden**." Then he pushed a large stone to the center of the lot.

3   "I have visited grand stone gardens. Let me put some rocks around the big stone. Then you will see the makings of a fine stone garden," said the old man. "Of course, to make this stone garden world-class, we might **paint** the rocks different colors."

4   Within an hour, the little rocks around the big stone glowed. They were painted with every color of the rainbow.

5   "Yes indeed," said the old man. "This is becoming a fine stone garden. Of course, to make a stone garden a garden, it should have plants. It should have flowers."

6   "I don't mind getting my hands dirty," said a young man. "I'll help dig up the ground. It's good exercise."

7   The people of Yancy Place worked all day in the garden. They worked the next day, too.

8   By that time, the old man had on his backpack. He took one last look at one of the truly finest stone gardens he had ever seen, and was on his way.

Word Map

What does the word eyesore mean?

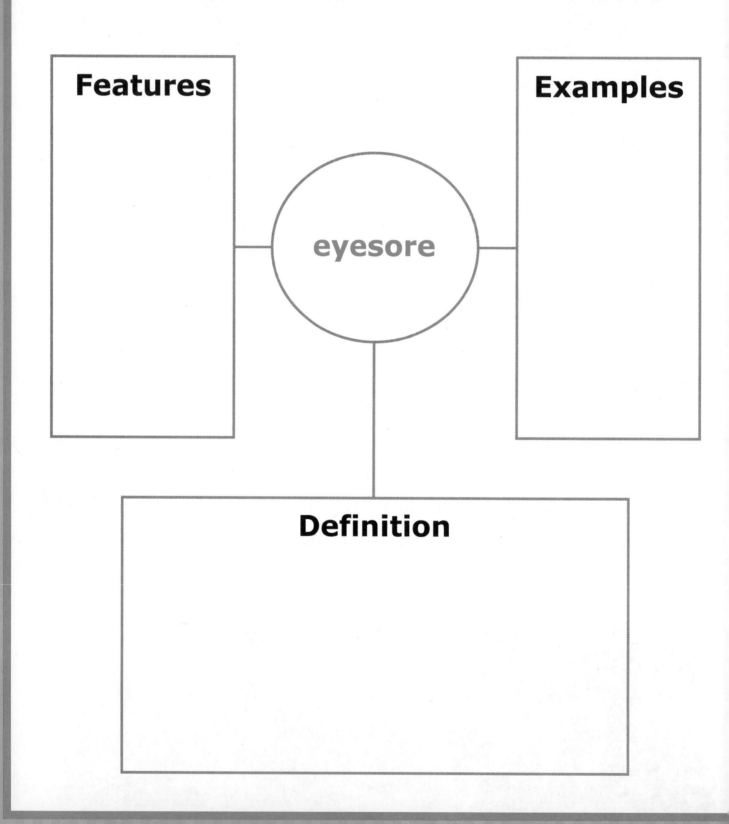

Features

Examples

eyesore

Definition

Recount Story Events

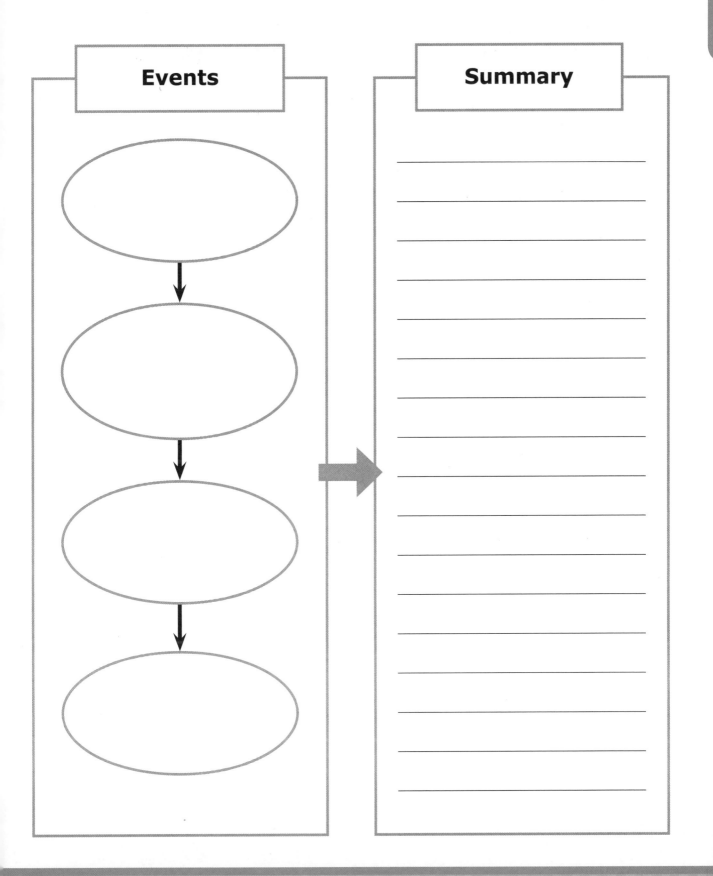

Events

Summary

Analyze Points of View

Character	Point of View
\n\n**old man**	
\n\n**people of Yancy Place**	

Compare and Contrast

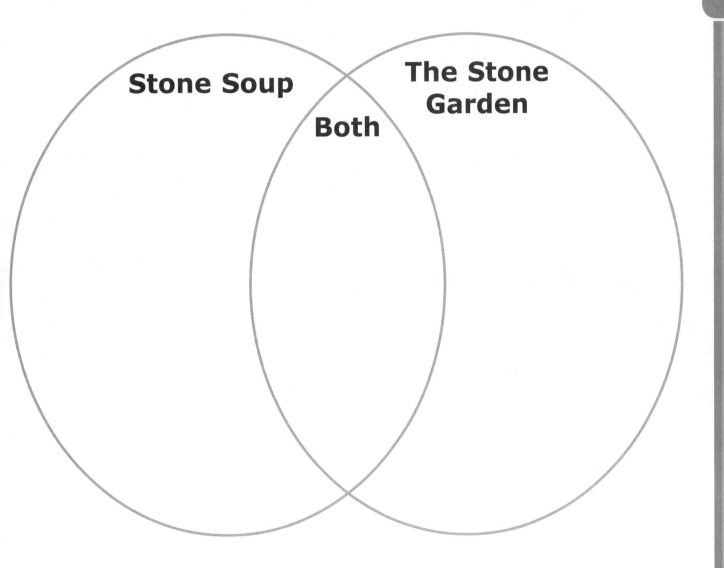

Stone Soup

Both

The Stone Garden

Essential Question

Where do ideas for inventions come from?

a robotic leg

My Content Objectives

- Build vocabulary related to where ideas come from
- Understand how ideas change our everyday lives

154

a computer

a dog wheelchair

155

Word	Examples
invented (in-VENT-ed)	She invented a new tool. He invented a new tool.
streetcar (STREET-kar)	The streetcar can stop. The streetcar can go.
windshield (WIND-sheeld)	The windshield has snow. The windshield has rain.
wipers (WY-perz)	The wipers are up. The wipers are down.

My Example	Definition
	invented, *verb* thought of and made first
	streetcar, *noun* a street-level train-like vehicle
	windshield, *noun* the large window at the front of a car
	wipers, *noun* tools that clear car windows so that drivers can see

A Woman with Vision

The first cars did not have **wipers**.

A woman was in a **streetcar**. The weather was bad.

The driver could not see.

The driver had to stop. He had to get out of the car.

Annotate

- Circle words that you have questions about.
- Underline the word that describes how to clear a windshield.

She saw him scrape the **windshield**.

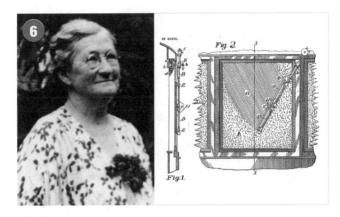

She had an idea.
She **invented** a new tool.

She invented wipers.

They cleared the windshield.

ThinkSpeakListen
Summarize why the woman invented wipers.

A Woman with Vision

Years ago, drivers had no way to see through their car's **windshield** when snow or rain blocked their view.

In 1903, Mary Anderson was riding in a **streetcar**.

The weather was unpleasant.

She noticed that drivers had to stop to scrape their windshields.

Then they had to stop again to rescrape their windshields.

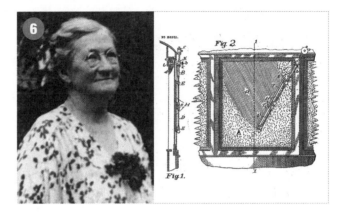

She thought there had to be a better way. She **invented** a window-clearing device.

The device let drivers control the **wipers** from inside their car.

The first wipers changed cars and driving forever.

ThinkSpeakListen

Retell the main idea of this text. Support the main idea with key details.

(handwritten annotations in margin: Notes)
Vision
blindfold
windshield
manual,
motorized

Mary Anderson invented wipers.

(handwritten at top: Inform / Topic)

A Woman with Vision

1   Would you ride in a car if the driver was wearing a blindfold? No way! Yet years ago, drivers had no way to see through their **windshield** when snow or rain blocked their view. Drivers had to stop and get out. They had to clear a spot on their windshield to see through and then drive on.

Years ago, a driver had to clear the windshield by hand.

Anderson was in a streetcar like this one when she got the idea that changed driving forever.

2   In 1903, Mary Anderson was riding in a **streetcar** in unpleasant weather. She noticed that the drivers had to stop to scrape and rescrape their windshields. She thought there had to be a better way. She **invented** a window-clearing device that drivers controlled from inside their cars. Those first **wipers** were manual, not motorized. But they changed cars and driving forever.

Compound Words

Compound Word	Word Parts	Meaning
windshield	wind shield	large window at the front of the car.
streetcar	street car	a street level car like vehica

Main Idea

Main Idea

Mary Anderson invented wipers.

Detail

She invented in 1903.

Detail

Before the invention drivers have to get down and scrape the wind shield.

Detail

First wipers were manual and not motorized.

windshied

windshield

Analyze Author's Purpose

Author's Statement	Facts and Details

Text Evidence Questions

1. Why did Mary Anderson invent windshield wipers?

She thought there has to be a solution to scrape the windshield.

Text Evidence:

She invented window clearing device that can be controlled from inside the car.

2. When and where did Mary Anderson get the idea for her invention?

In 1903 Mary got the idea in a streetcar.

Text Evidence:

Drivers have to get down and scrape.

3. How did the first wipers work?

First wipers were manual.

Text Evidence:

Those first wipers were manual, not moterized.

4. What impact did the first wipers have on cars and driving?

All cars now have wipers. These days all cars have automatic wipers.

Text Evidence:

But they changed the cars and driving forever.

Word	Examples	
farmers (FAR-merz)	 These are farmers.	 These are farmers.
inventor (in-VEN-ter)	 This is an inventor.	 This is an inventor.
lightbulb (LITE-bulb)	 A lightbulb is shining.	 A lightbulb is bright.
telegraph (TEH-leh-graf)	 This is a telegraph.	 This is a telegraph.

My Example	Definition
	farmers, *noun* people who raise animals and grow crops
	inventor, *noun* someone who thinks of and builds new things
	lightbulb, *noun* a glass bulb that gives off light using electricity
	telegraph, *noun* a system for sending messages over distances

Famous Inventors

by Margaret McNamara

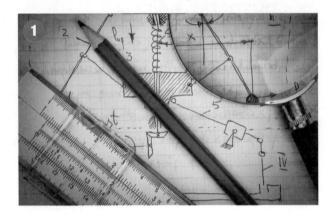

An **inventor** makes something new.

Thomas Edison was an inventor. He invented the **lightbulb**.

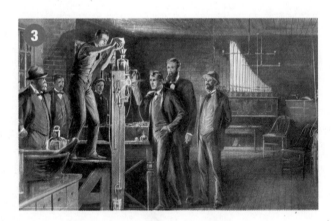

He also invented the phonograph and the movie camera.

Alexander Graham Bell was an inventor. He worked on the **telegraph**.

Annotate
- Circle words that you have questions about.
- Underline who invented the lightbulb.

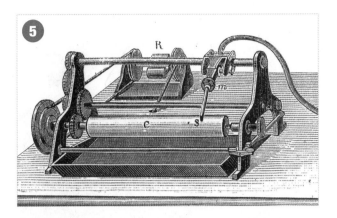

A telegraph sends messages.

Bell invented the telephone.

George Washington Carver
was an inventor. He taught
farmers how to grow peanuts.

He invented uses for peanuts
and sweet potatoes.

ThinkSpeakListen

Tell the text's main idea. Give a detail that supports the main idea.

Famous Inventors

by Margaret McNamara

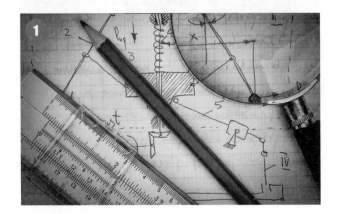

An **inventor** is someone who creates something new. An inventor finds new ways to do things.

Thomas Edison and his workers came up with more than 1,000 inventions. He invented the first electric **lightbulb**.

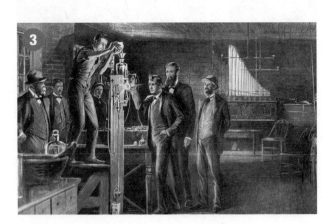

He also invented the phonograph. He invented the first movie camera, too.

In 1872, Alexander Graham Bell worked to make a better **telegraph**.

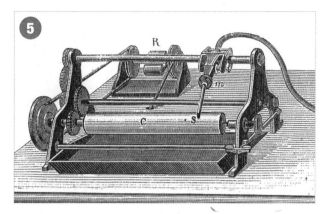

A telegraph sends and receives coded sound messages. The sounds are beeps and clicks.

Bell invented a machine that sent and received the human voice. In 1876, Bell invented the first telephone.

George Washington Carver taught students and **farmers** how to grow peanut plants.

He invented hundreds of new uses for peanuts and sweet potatoes.

ThinkSpeakListen

Tell which inventions we still use today.

Famous Inventors

by Margaret McNamara

Notes

1   An **inventor** is someone who creates something new. An inventor also finds new ways to do things. An inventor works to solve problems.

2   Thomas Alva Edison loved to make new things. During his lifetime, Edison and his workers came up with more than 1,000 inventions. He is best known for inventing the first long-lasting electric **lightbulb**. He also invented the phonograph. The first phonograph made recordings of people talking or singing. He invented the first movie camera.

Thomas Alva Edison   Alexander Graham Bell   George Washington Carver

3   Alexander Graham Bell had a lifelong interest in communication. In 1872, Bell began to tutor deaf children. He also worked to make a better **telegraph**. A telegraph sends and receives coded sound messages. A telegraph was the only way people could "talk" to each other from far away. Bell wanted to invent a machine that would send and receive the human voice. In 1876, Bell showed the world the first telephone.

4   George Washington Carver was the first black student at Iowa State Agricultural College. Carver studied everything he could about plants. After college, Carver became a teacher. He taught students and **farmers** about plants. Carver taught farmers how to grow peanut and sweet potato plants. He invented hundreds of new uses for peanuts and sweet potatoes.

5   Some inventors make things that change the way people live. Other inventors find better ways to do things. These inventors all changed the world for the better.

Word Web

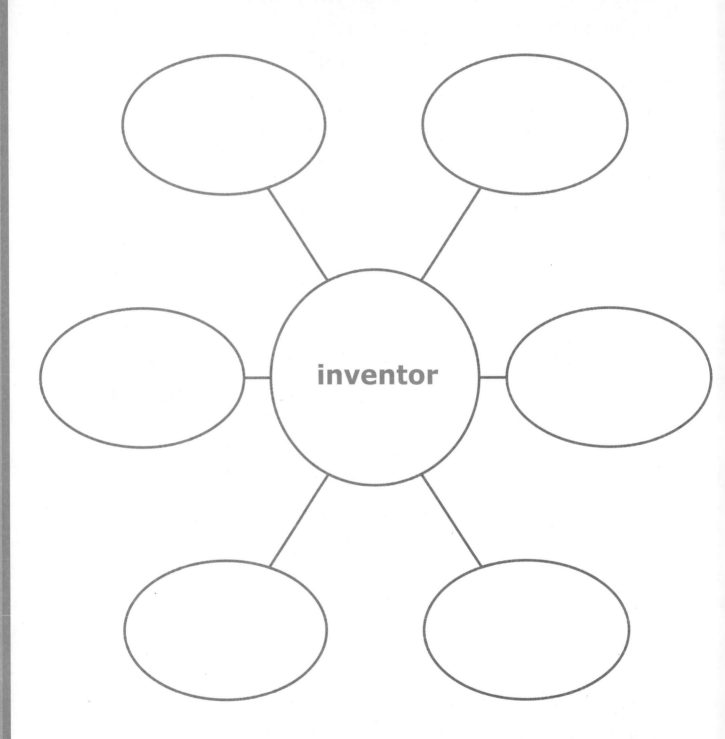

Main Idea

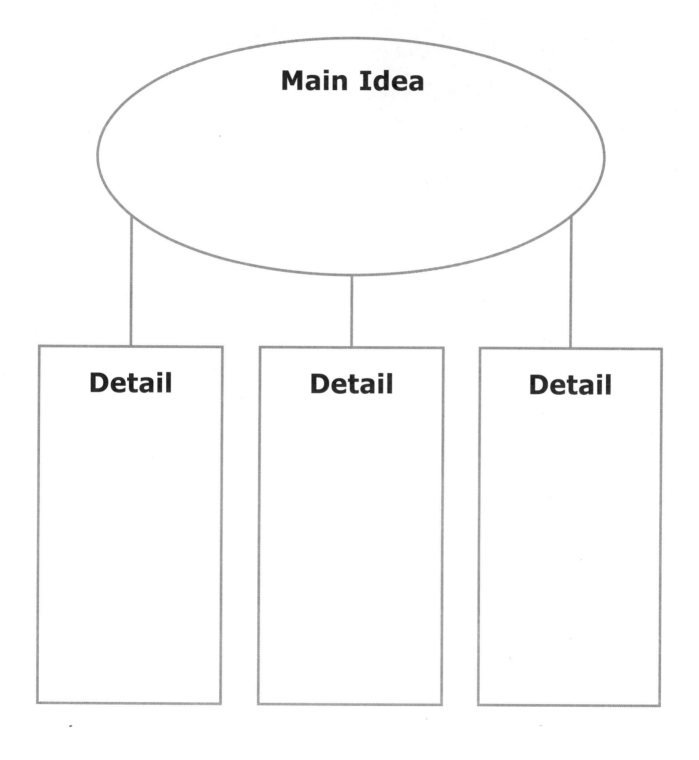

Main Idea

Detail

Detail

Detail

Use Graphic Features

1 **What did Thomas Edison invent?**

_____

_____

_____

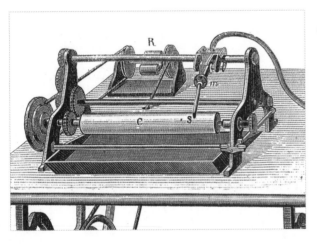

2 **What is a telegraph?**

_____

_____

_____

_____

3 **How did George Washington Carver help farmers?**

_____

_____

Compare and Contrast

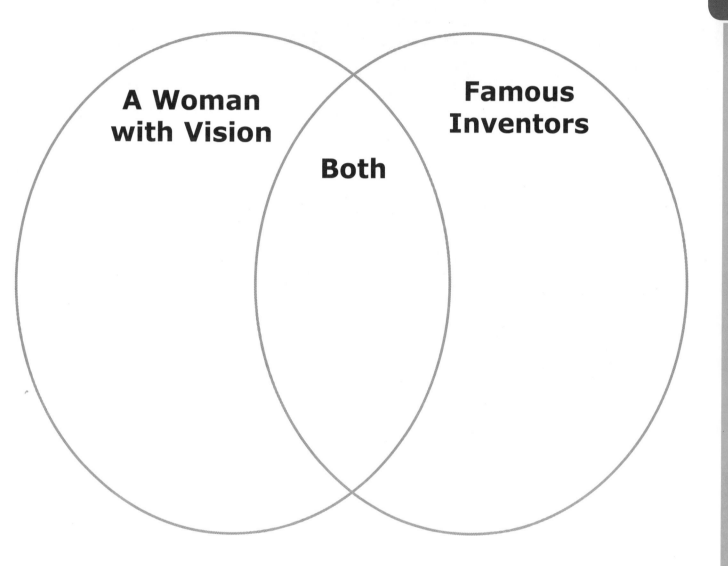

A Woman with Vision

Famous Inventors

Both

Word	Examples	
computer mouse (kum-PYOO-ter MOWS)	 This is a computer mouse.	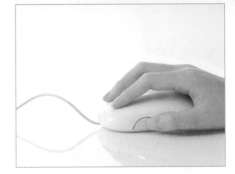 This is a computer mouse.
nickname (NIK-name)	 This robot has a nickname.	 This robot has a nickname.
robot (ROH-baht)	 A robot can help.	 A robot can move.
sick (SIK)	 This child is sick.	 This student is sick.

My Example	Definition
	computer mouse, *noun* a device used to control a computer
	nickname, *noun* another name given to a person, place, or thing
	robot, *noun* a machine that partly looks and acts like a human being
	sick, *adjective* not well; having an illness

Robots Go to School

by Kathy Kafer

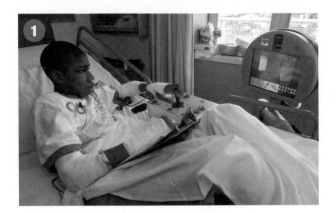

This boy is too **sick** to go to school.

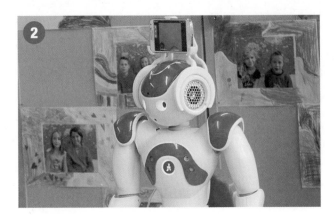

A **robot** goes to school for him.

The robot has a video screen.

The robot has wheels.

Annotate
- Circle words that you have questions about.
- Underline why robots go to school.

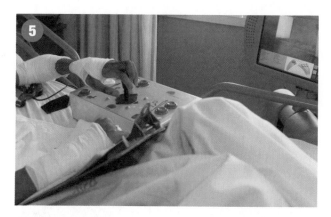

This boy uses a **computer mouse** to move his robot.

This robot has a **nickname**.

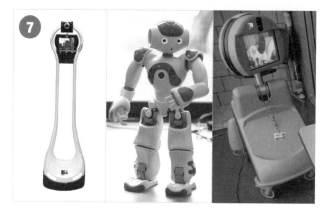

These robots cannot climb stairs or open doors.

The robot lets teachers see the students who are too sick to go to school.

ThinkSpeakListen

Describe how a robot helps children who are too sick to go to school.

Robots Go to School

by Kathy Kafer

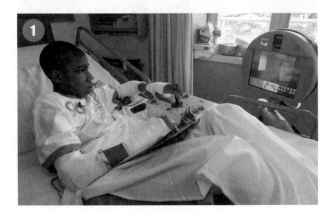

Some children are too **sick** to go to school. Now, **robots** can go to school for them.

These special robots help children who cannot be in a classroom.

The robot has a video screen. The student can press a button to answer a question. A light flashes on the robot.

The robot has wheels. It can travel up and down the hallways. The robot can line up with the children.

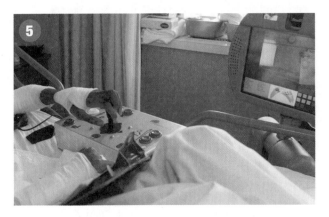

A child can move the robot with a **computer mouse**. A signal is sent through the Internet to the robot.

Children who use school robots often give them **nicknames**.

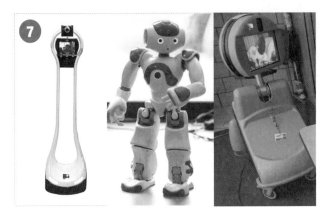

The robots cannot climb stairs or open doors. When the Internet is down, the child who is sick cannot tell the robot what to do.

The robots let teachers keep in touch with the students who are sick. Teachers can even give jobs to children at home.

ThinkSpeakListen

Do you have robots at school?

Remember
to annotate
as you read.

Robots Go to School

by Kathy Kafer

1   Some children are too **sick** to go to school. Now **robots** can go to school for them. These special robots help children who cannot be in a classroom. These special robots let children who can't go to school feel as if they are there.

2   The robot has a video screen. A student's face shows on that screen. The student can press a button to answer a question. A light flashes on the robot. The teacher knows to call on that child.

3   The robot has wheels. It can move around a classroom. It can travel up and down the hallways. The robot can even line up with the children during a fire drill.

4   A child moves the robot with a **computer mouse**. A signal is sent through the Internet to the robot. And the robot sends videos back to the child.

5 The children who use school robots often give them **nicknames**. Some children dress up their robots. The robot might wear the child's favorite T-shirt.

6 Teachers like having these robots, too. The robots let teachers keep in touch with their sick students. Teachers can even give classroom jobs to children at home.

7 Of course, school robots are not real children. They cannot think or talk on their own. Those children who use robots still have to pay attention and turn in their homework assignments.

8 Robots have limitations. They cannot climb stairs or open doors. When the Internet is down, the child who is sick cannot tell the robot what to do. The robot stops moving and talking. The child can no longer see what is going on at school.

Word Map

What does the word robot mean?

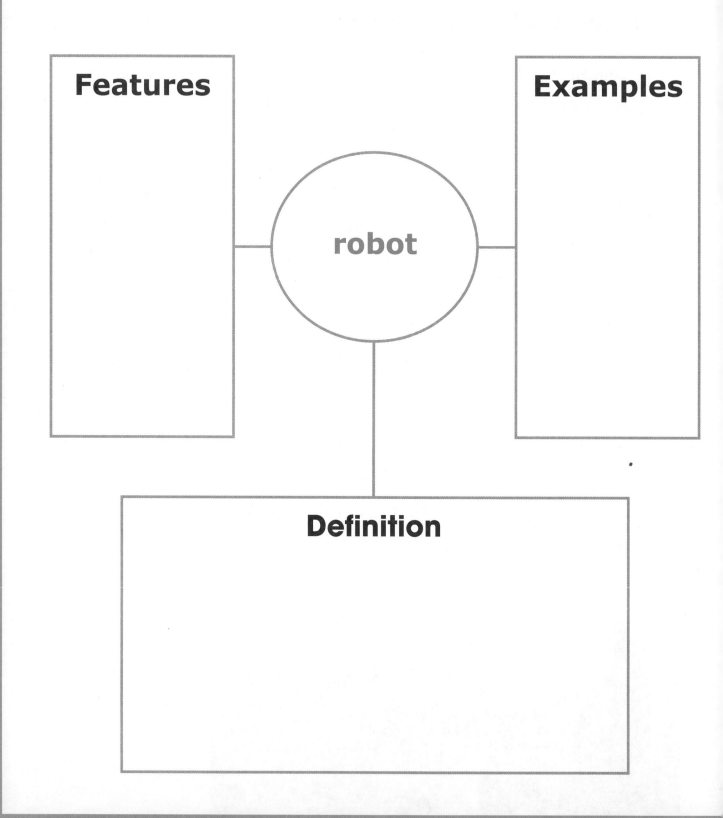

Features

Examples

robot

Definition

Main Idea

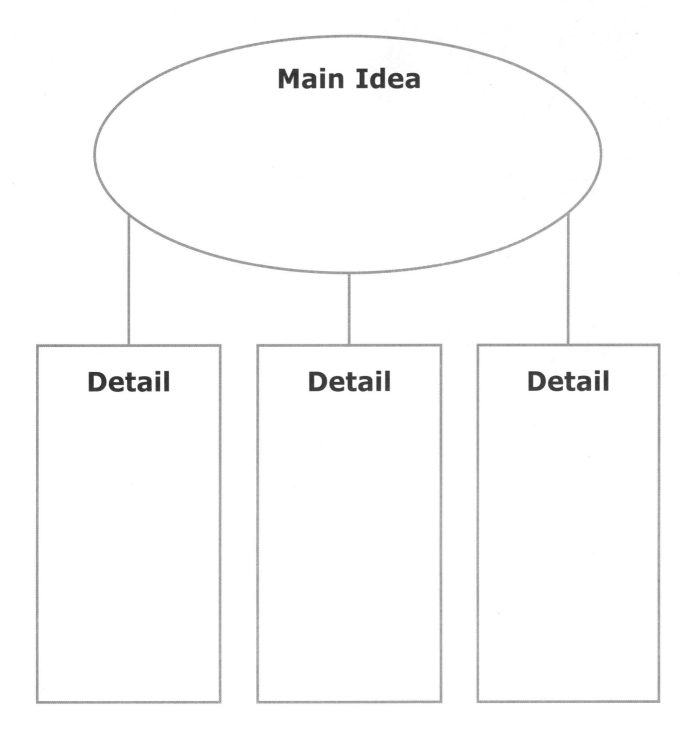

Use Graphic Features

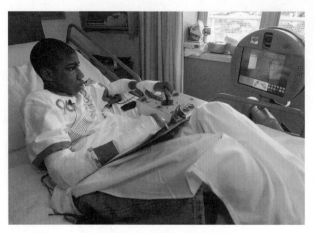

1 Why do robots go to school?

_____

_____

_____

2 What can robots do at school?

_____

_____

_____

3 How do robots help teachers?

_____

_____

_____

Analyze Reasons and Evidence

Why are school robots important?

Reasons	Evidence